ADVANCE PRAISE FOR *Making Love While Farming*

"I was hooked from the very first line of Deb Habib and Ricky Baruch's beautiful book, *Making Love While Farming*. In a time when so much of what makes our world wondrous and just is being threatened, Habib and Baruch's book is a hopeful and joyous antidote. Through personal narrative interwoven with practical advice (and delicious recipes!), the authors take us on an unforgettable journey that is riveting, funny, and always deeply moving and down to earth."

*Mira Bartók, author of* The New York Times
*bestselling memoir,* The Memory Palace

"*Making Love While Farming* is a practical beacon of inspiration and hope for humanity...an invaluable gift whose timeliness cannot be overstated. This is not a feel-good book. It is a get-out-and-do-good book. Deb and Ricky have demonstrated convincingly that making love and making a difference can be and should be synonymous."

*Greg Watson, two term Massachusetts Commissioner of
Agriculture, Director for Policy and Systems Design
at the Schumacher Center for a New Economics*

"Farming and loving, passion and purpose: words that do not always fit seamlessly, but Deb Habib and Ricky Baruch have managed to bring them together beautifully in this inspiring testament to their life's work. Weaving common sense, humor, and love, this is a truly delicious potpourri of thoughts on sustainable farming, anti-war activism, healthy eating, and committed solidarity for people and the earth. I know you will treasure this book as much as I treasure them."

*Sonia Nieto, Professor Emerita, College of Education,
University of Massachusetts, Amherst*

"*Making Love While Farming* belongs right next to the Nearing's *Living the Good Life*, with a major difference. Ricky and Deb not only model how they personally live the good life, but also share their great commitment to building healthy communities and directly increasing access to fresh, healthy food. If you want to be inspired, read this book!"

*Tom Wessels, Terrestrial Ecologist, author of* The Myth
of Progress and Reading the Forested Landscape:
A Natural History of New England

"I've always thought that the most amazing tales are the ones based on people's real lives. This sweet book is no exception. Beautifully written, the essays inspire and entertain, while being a wealth of information for those interested in creating a more thoughtful, sustainable future. These stories filled me with gratitude and hope that the human race can create good communities if our hearts are committed and we aren't afraid of a little hard work. In their words ...'*sacrifice* and *sacred* share a holy root, and the distinction between them is often permeable when such choices bring you closer to yourself, others, and nature.' So true!"

*Roxanne Swentzell, Sculptor, Flowering Tree Permaculture Institute co-founder, and author of* The Pueblo Food Experience Cookbook: Whole Food of Our Ancestors

"This is a revolutionary story, the account of a beautiful journey of one family discovering the rich rewards of conscientious right livelihood, then experiencing the abundant fruits of their joyful, persistent hard work, while earnestly sharing their organic philosophy with the larger community as an example for others."

*S. Brian Willson, Vietnam veteran, peace activist, and author of* Blood on the Tracks

"Seeds of Solidarity founders Deb Habib and Ricky Baruch weave their decades of experience with sustainable farming and community revitalization into a compelling narrative that offers practical, concrete advice about how we can work together to empower others and change how our country thinks about food."

*Congressman Jim McGovern*

"Deb and Ricky's life is both a prayer and an answer to our prayers. Their work to heal our relationships to land and each other is the tangible manifestation of their love. Bearing witness to the grit, ingenuity, determination, and passion that birthed Seeds of Solidarity gave us the confidence to manifest Soul Fire Farm. Both practical and poetic *Making Love While Farming* is a road map to creating a life of joy and meaning."

*Leah Penniman, author of* Farming While Black: Soul Fire Farm's Practical Guide to Liberation on the Land

# MAKING LOVE
## *While* FARMING

### *A Field Guide to a Life of Passion & Purpose*

Ricky Baruch and Deb Habib

*Levellers Press*

AMHERST, MASSACHUSETTS

*Levellers Press* • Amherst, Massachusetts

ISBN 978-1-945473-86-9

# Contents

*Gratitude for*

*Our ancestors*

*Our parents who first grew us; our families*

*Our mentors*

*Our son — follow your heart and thrive*

*Our beloved community of support*

# Introduction

We didn't know that the night we first slept together under grapevines and stars would be anything more than a sweet one-night stand on a thin blanket in the dewy grass. Or perhaps we didn't really think about it much at all, being simply caught in the magic moment of having found ourselves (and each other) at the New Alchemy Institute on Cape Cod in the early 1980s. We were both just shy of twenty-two, born three months and one hundred miles apart in 1962, emerging headfirst into an era of protest and pacifism, counterculture, and creativity. Our trajectories crossed for a night, and then for forever.

That first summer of love we volunteered in the gardens by day and waited tables and landscaped to pay the rent. New Alchemy was a visionary and pioneering research center in organic agriculture, aquaculture and bioshelter design. Hooked on growing food, we transformed a small, unused plot there into our own small market garden. We slathered some paint on a scrap of wood and wrote: "This Garden is Planted in Solidarity with Those Around the World Helping to Feed the People." It remains a bit of a mystery as to why we chose those words above all others we could have extracted from the plethora of experience, books and fascinating people we relished day and night during that most amazing era of our self-directed learning.

We didn't have reason to imagine that our first summer together would lead to a year, and that after that year we'd part ways, moving many miles apart. We sustained a friendship as we cultivated independent lives each with their

Our first market garden together. (New Alchemy Institute, Falmouth, Massachusetts, 1984)

good and hard times, before finally reuniting to commit to our shared vision ten years after that lovely and fateful first night.

We simultaneously planned our wedding and the eight-month spiritual and political pilgrimage from Auschwitz to Hiroshima that would follow. We hadn't yet found the land where we would ultimately build an off-the-grid home, raise a family, and transform a barren forest clearing into a vibrant farm and non-profit organization with the mantra "Grow Food Everywhere" that would come to reach and teach hundreds of thousands of people. But, as we headed into what we called the "War Zone Honeymoon Tour," we invoked a name to hold the essence of what we would create together upon return, a name cultivated a decade earlier in our first garden together: Seeds of Solidarity.

The journey depicted in this book has been deeply romantic and at times incredibly challenging. We've had our share of pain and pitfalls, despair and detours over three and a half decades. We feel profound gratitude for the precious gift of deep love and shared vision that grows each day alongside abundant crops at Seeds of Solidarity, surrounded by wonderful neighbors on Chestnut Hill Road in Orange, Massachusetts.

*Making Love While Farming* recounts stories of love and livelihood. Over a period of several years, we sat and wrote together one morning each week, carving sacred time from the responsibilities of a farm, non-profit organization, huge annual festival, community volunteerism, friendships, and family. We offer this book not just as a collection of our honest tales of life and love on the farm, but also as a guide for personal reflection, healthy relationships, and more resilient communities. A 'field guide' section concludes each chapter with a sequence of activities, tools, and meditative practices. These are designed to add ritual to daily life, cultivate a loving, spirited existence, and promote a more purposeful time on the planet. For those still hungry for inspiration, the culminating chapter is filled with seasonal recipes from the Seeds of Solidarity Farm table.

We hope you will use this book in ways most meaningful to you. Our stories reflect the power of relationship and community to transform vision into reality, and we hope that you will enjoy this book with partners, friends, neighbors and colleagues to create such stories of your own. There is much to be gathered about leading a self-created and meaningful life from the pages within without even having to plant a seed in a garden—although we highly recommend it!

This would not be a book worthy of reading without those who have been a part of Seeds of Solidarity: toddlers, teens, those incarcerated, farmers, friends, mentors and interns are all part of the magnificent web of those that have enriched our lives, and sown seeds of solidarity in both simple and transformative ways. Some may be disappointed (others, relieved) to find that *Making Love While Farming* does not feature a series of Kamasutra sexual poses for the great outdoors. But it is our greatest hope that the love infused in these pages radiates widely to inspire many beautiful, resilient lives and communities.

# Chapter One

# Journey of a Self-Created Life: Open Hearts, Fertile Dreams

## *Giving Blood in Baghdad*

The UN helicopter overhead riled the desert sand and rippled the monks' yellow robes. We were surprised when they landed, having thought they were only surveying the scene of our diverse and somewhat disheveled group, halfway on its pilgrimage from Auschwitz to Hiroshima. It was early 1995. Scattered around the arid landscape were the rusted remains of cars that were carpet-bombed as they sought return to Iraq from Kuwait during the first of a devastating series of Gulf Wars.

I had noticed a peculiar ridge of sand in the distance beyond the heat haze as we walked the scorched road south of Basra, Iraq. It was the only thing of its height for miles around, and clearly not a geologic phenomenon. Many meters below us swirled the viscous blackness of Rumaila, one of the largest oil fields in the world. We learned that ridge had been created with large bulldozers funded by the U.S. government and recently moved by the same. Marking a border between Iraq and Kuwait, the ridge had been moved to bring more of that oil field into the domain of Kuwait, a U.S. oil ally. Unbeknownst to our group, this clandestine and political border move meant that our ceremony at the end of the Highway of Death (which connected Kuwait and Iraq) was now in Kuwait, and we were without the visas to be there.

A man in an olive jacket heavily decorated with military emblem descended the four metal steps of the copter and strolled towards us as our prayer circle leader John Schuchardt turned to greet him. I checked my assumptions, more used to those interrupting vigils or protests being white men rather than the African UN officer who stood calmly before us. John is a seasoned peace activist, Plowshares Eight member, and former attorney and Marine officer who became temporarily known worldwide for barging into the Kennebunkport church of George H. W. Bush, crying out "Stop the Killing" fervently and repeatedly as security carried him out. John's animated speech was concluded by a polite handshake with the UN official before turning to us to inform us that we were committing a border violation and should move our circle thirty meters north to continue our prayers.

Days earlier on the well-worn bus from Amman, Jordan to its border with Iraq, we folded origami cranes as best we could as the bus dodged potholes. Along with building interfaith Peace Pagodas and carrying forth the tradition of prayerful walk as a form of nonviolent activism, the Nipponzan Myohoji Buddhist order folded and gifted these in memory of Sadako Sasaki, a young girl who folded cranes as a symbol of hope after being poisoned by radiation during the bombing of Hiroshima. While a small strand was offered to someone who had provided us with food or a place to sleep at the end of our long days of walking, most of those cranes we folded would be strung into cascades of one thousand to leave in deeply significant places. We had left one at the gates of Auschwitz, and would leave another at the Almira bomb shelter, where, in a Baghdad suburb, hundreds of people were killed by U.S. bombs dropped dead center over their refuge. As we folded the colorful squares on the ragged bus to the border, an idea arose among our equally ragged group hailing from Japan, the U.S., Germany, Chile, Costa Rica and Thailand: we decided to give blood. We would give in Iraq because it was very likely needed in the hospitals given the unethical U.S. sanctions restricting medical supplies. If we made it across the border, that is.

We sat in the large cinder block room at the Karameh border crossing, waiting, as had been the case often over the last few months, for hours. Usually we would nap, write, patch blisters on swollen feet, repack knapsacks, or fold cranes as we waited. No one was napping that day: we were waiting to learn if Ramsey Clark, who was U.S. Attorney General under President Johnson and who had vocally condemned the

Bush administration for crimes against humanity, had managed from a distance to negotiate our passage over the border and five hundred kilometers onward to Baghdad.

Ricky and I made sure to stay together as a few men ushered forty of us out and into a caravan of dilapidated vehicles. We rode for hours, crammed into hot, old station wagons on dusty roads that eventually turned into broken asphalt. In fragmented English our Iraqi escorts pointed out buildings, power grids, and roads broken and burned by bombs. As we approached Baghdad, they showed off the exquisite architecture—some ancient, some modern and gleaming—punctuated by billboards of a smiling Saddam Hussein holding out a butterfly to a small child.

There was a guard on each floor, 24/7, of the Baghdad Hotel. Mustapha Samson stood poised near our room. He had been working in Kuwait to make money for his family back home in Somalia and was now unable to return to either place. He and Ricky made fast friends.

Our group was never without guides from the Iraqi government department of peace, solidarity and friendship (an office I've yet to see come out of our own White House). We told them we would like to give blood while in Baghdad. On the appointed day, the Red Cross set up a very professional clinic in a large room in the hotel. I still say it was the best blood I've ever given. The only thing lacking—lacking in the entire country, along with any fresh food—was the usual glass of post-donation orange juice to ease the blood sugar drop. Ricky had headed back to our room while I walked the five flights of stairs down to the lobby, where I was quickly approached by one of the guards.

"Is your husband alright?"

"He's fine, thank you," I replied, assuming his inquiry was yet another of the plethora of diverse, lovely greetings we encountered throughout our travels. Phrases like 'May God travel with you,' 'May your dreams be good,' fill the heart much more than 'Have a nice day.' But as it turned out, after giving blood, Ricky had promptly collapsed against the door to our room, where his new friend Mustapha had quickly righted his slumped form and helped him inside to rest. News had traveled as fast as it had taken me to walk down the stairs. By the time I walked (a bit more quickly) up to our room, he was restored. But the country would not be, nor could we imagine then that another decade and a half of bloodshed and devastation would follow.

Ricky and I are often asked what we give up to live off-the-grid. Witnessing the impact of war in Iraq solidified our resolve to reduce our reliance on fossil fuels and do our small part to not feed oil wars. Our early adult years before our marriage were a quest to gather skills to grow food and live with renewable energy. On a small clearing just off a dirt road that had been logged and abandoned about twenty-five years prior, we sowed our first seeds and poured our first building piers at Seeds of Solidarity a year after our return from the eight-month pilgrimage. There was no power; we charged our two cordless power tools in our old truck lighter. Ricky's building skills and great neighbors helped us raise the walls of our off-the-grid home. Having little money for machinery or labor to help transform marginal, stripped forest into farmland steered us towards no-till techniques that made rich soil, fostered life within, and helped mitigate the impacts of climate change that devastate farmers worldwide.

Modest arrays of solar panels now provide all of our electricity for home and farm. True, living off-the-grid requires an attentive awareness of use in relation to what the day and season offers. Yet 'sacrifice' and 'sacred' share a holy root, and the distinction between them is often permeable when such choices bring you closer to yourself, others, and nature. Living off-the-grid is not without escapades and challenges. And farming is already filled with escapades and challenges. But we sacrifice very little compared to our brothers and sisters around the world living in war, as refugees, or in poverty in our own community. The sun is the source of all life in our daily lives. Each light clicked on to start the day, the coolness of the breakfast yogurt, a family video watched curled on the couch, and the pumping of water from a deep well to irrigate the fields and greenhouses filled with crops that we raise for food and livelihood becomes a gift.

# A Universe-Arranged Marriage

When I graduated high school in New Rochelle, New York in 1980, I knew I wasn't ready for college. I was drawn to the sea and to marine biology, so I volunteered on a research vessel, worked on a friend's boat, and crewed on Pete Seeger's Hudson *Clearwater* sloop. In between, I washed dishes at a local deli for money. People now call this a 'gap year,' but back then this made my parents freak out. My older brothers had disappeared into ashrams and I guess the folks were hoping I'd take a more traditional route to balance out their turban-clad yogi offspring. I eventually found a school down in South Jersey that seemed right for me.

At this point in my life I was pretty focused, having quit smoking pot. At Stockton State College I took marine science classes, exercised a lot, and made a few friends that would become lifelong. My childhood idol was Jacques Cousteau and I had dreams of working with whales and dolphins. But my college advisor steered me away from that field, saying there was no money in it. It was 1981 and the search for oil and marine deposits was hot, so he was leading me towards marine geology. At this young age an authoritative voice can really impact your life and sometimes even bust your dreams. I had no interest in discovering oil deposits, and my performance in the organic chemistry classes he encouraged affirmed that my time at college was coming to an end. Somewhere in me, the radical idea of solar energy ignited my passion and I decided to take on an independent solar energy project.

Looking back, I wonder about those divine forces at play. While researching solar energy, or maybe while looking into fish farming, or perhaps while working on the *Clearwater*—I'm not sure—I came across the New Alchemy Institute. By then, I was ready to get out of college and find my own way, and figured I'd write to New Alchemy asking about housing and such. Meanwhile, Deb was already at New Alchemy as an intern, also having left college after two years in search of more real-life experience. Having gotten there on pure luck, with her mentor Greg Watson spontaneously picking up and replying to her letter, she saw that there was no one to respond to mail from other inquiring apprentices. She had asked Denise, the office manager and beloved godmother of all at New Alchemy, if she could reply to other seekers, at least with a basic form letter. Soon after sending off my letter I received one in return, though not with the answer I was hoping for. Deb had interpreted my question about housing as an interest in a housing design internship, where all I was interested in was a place to live while I volunteered. Nonetheless, a letter back signaled a 'go' for me and I now knew the name of at least one person at New Alchemy: Debbie Habib. I left college and went on a wild adventure with two friends to Europe. I ended up broke, and worked on a farm in England until I had enough money for airfare back to the States.

Two days after returning to the U.S. I hitchhiked to Cape Cod and showed up at the New Alchemy doorstep with my backpack, a Walk for Peace patch sewn to its top flap. I arrived at New Alchemy and asked for Debbie Habib, but alas, she had left for California.

Someone handed me a shovel. I got to work and made myself at home getting into the scene, working in the fields all day while learning from visionary mentors about growing food, renewable energy, and fish farming, then reading about these well into the night. After about ten months, Deb returned from working on farms on the west coast. I initially thought she was involved with the head gardener, my new friend Pete, so I remained a little distant as we got to know each other. Soon after her arrival we ended up at a party and the energy began flowing between us. I asked "What about Pete?" and she replied, "What about Pete? We're just good friends." I still have various sensations of that first romantic night, how things felt as we slept together under the grape arbor. There was already a feeling of comfort and familiarity.

I sometimes wonder: when your physical body dies, will you be able to see all the experiences in life you thought were just coincidence suddenly as a huge web of synchronicity? I can't help but believe that the universe brought us together as it knew this was going to be a healthy symbiotic relationship for the planet. Sure, there was the usual young twenties lust going on as we came together that first night, but also a knowing that there was something deeper there. What a perfect fertile ground, to meet at New Alchemy—both of us so inspired by similar interests. There was such a special energy there, what with everyone so passionately committed to humanitarian and environmental causes. We had the opportunity to be among many great visionaries, and to be a part of a place and movement so energized and filled with possibility. This added to the romance. I was so comfortable with Deb; it was not full of crazy drama like other relationships I had known until then.

During our two years together at New Alchemy, Deb and I were together but also independent and not strictly monogamous. She went off to Europe and India, and while away both of us did a little exploring with others to get that out of our system. In 1987, I left New Alchemy to seek and ultimately purchase a farm with our mutual friend Stuart, landing near Ithaca, New York. Deb headed to a new chapter of life in Western Massachusetts. We were apart for six years, reuniting every so often when neither of us was in a committed relationship to come together for a weekend of reconnection and romance. The universe gave us time to explore but kept us connected. In 1993, nine years after first meeting, circumstances in our lives once again drew us strongly back together. This time it felt different; the embrace felt as if it was meant to last. For the really big decisions in life, sometimes there is less thinking and simply a true knowing of the right path to take. It was time to create a sacred life together.

We were meant to come together in this lifetime as two children following their hearts in an often-heartless culture. Together, we saw and deeply felt the problems of humanity, and had the passion and work ethic to carry forward what we had gathered since coming together at the New Alchemy Institute, a place that inspired and united us with lasting and profound direction.

## Meanwhile...

At seventeen I moved from New Jersey to Colorado. I had abbreviated my high school years and saved money landscaping to fulfill my dreams of going to college out West. In high school, the class that best held my attention was architectural drawing. Aside from a teacher who regularly stared down the shirts of the few girls in his classes, it was a good place to envision, focus, and draw. At my drafting table, I let my mind fill with ideas, let pencil lines become the shape of sun and plant-filled buildings, and dreamed of life on my own.

With this musty high school classroom and worn drafting table as my inspiration, I enrolled in the College of Environmental Design in Boulder and flew out there alone and sight unseen a few months short of my eighteenth birthday with my parents' bewildered support. As instructed, I bought rolls of vellum, an architectural ruler, and drawing pens in seven different point sizes at a supply store next to a Japanese noodle house. Tools in my backpack, I'd head to the design studios on campus that remained lit with student energy until three in the morning. In these spacious, industrious studios, I sipped bancha tea with a pale macrobiotic woman at the next drawing table, engineered contraptions made solely with spirals, and mixed epoxy to simulate streams flowing through a scale model of dwellings constructed of twigs and stones. For money, I flipped burgers and served Coors Light in the campus center's Alfred Packer Grill—named for a famous mountaineer-turned-cannibal—and worked on the grounds crew. I spent hours sweeping the well-populated steps around the fountains on central campus in work made less monotonous by my budding interest in meditation and the occasional joint offered by the students with no need for work-study jobs who lounged there.

While a few of my professors were radical innovators, most were not. Dissatisfied with the rigid aspects of the program, friends and I created our own informal weekend school. We called it Anbau, suggested by my friend Hans for the German word's meaning of 'extension.' As an extension to what we were (or were not) learning in school, every couple of months we would find somewhere beautiful to go for a weekend. Twenty of us, all studying architecture, art, or engineering would come together in the spirit of teaching whatever we were inspired to share. We learned from each other's informal workshops, be it batik, astronomy, pie making, yoga, or how to change spark plugs. This simple yet profound concept of everyone as teacher and learner would remain with me and inform much to come.

While I was grappling with some dissatisfaction with my program at the University itself, a teaching assistant became my friend and mentor and invited me to his home city of Denver to do community organizing. We knocked on doors collecting input from Latino residents on their neighborhood hopes, punctuated with lunches of the best ever green chili burritos from the original food trucks. While at first exciting, the structure of university was beginning to give way to the authenticity of community-based and hands-on learning.

In my second year of studies, while on a weekend road trip to New Mexico with friends, I pulled out my sketchpad to complete an assignment on trees for a graphic drawing class. Sunset caught a magnificent pinyon pine, casting a gorgeous purple glow that I enhanced with watercolor on my sketch of its gnarled branches. I felt really good about it. My professor, seeking architectural drawing style and specificity, did not. He marred it with a bold F. I knew in that moment and after two good years of college that I was ready to move on.

I also knew it was time to return to a place I had been at age thirteen that had rocked my internal world. In the summer of 1976, the cover of *The New York Times Magazine* had depicted a photo of a group of longhaired folks gathered around what I would later learn were solar algae ponds in a geodesic dome. I would also learn, during the Saturday farm tour that my adventuring parents dragged me and my siblings to, that these people were brilliant scientists who also got their hands dirty daily as they built everything from tool sheds to windmill towers. They were forward thinkers that fastidiously counted insect species and trialed natural fertilizers for some of the first ever experiments carried out in the emerging field of organic agriculture. I learned that they shared the food they grew with visitors like us under a mulberry tree, and that they spent their days working hard while envisioning the creation of a saner world.

As a child, I had not yet witnessed anything like this; something deep inside me had moved and I kept that seed of possibility safely embedded. When I decided to leave college, I knew where I wanted to go. Little did I know that the letter I had sent to the New Alchemy Institute, ("a small international organization dedicated to research and education on behalf of humanity and the planet") seeking an internship had been placed onto a pile of many on the desk of Greg Watson. Greg was New Alchemy's education director as well as a Buckminster Fuller devotee who would later become Massachusetts Commissioner of Agriculture, the first African American man to do so. In a moment of challenge from his intern to do a better job of answering his letters, he randomly picked mine and wrote right back. I left college as well as a challenging relationship in Colorado (unfortunately while pregnant, a story for another day) and returned to this place that had left such an early imprint on my being. I signed on for a three-month internship that lengthened into a life-transforming year as I learned and worked among some of the finest and most visionary ecologists and social thinkers of our era.

It was only my adventurous spirit that sent me off on a road trip to California and the University of California Santa Cruz Farm and Garden Project where my best Boulder buddy Marshall was an apprentice. I lived in the hills above Santa Cruz while helping to establish a school garden in Davenport, a town of early organic farmers, coastal hippies, surfers, and Mexicans working the artichoke fields. I then worked on farms up the west coast, traveling with my dog Jasper in a 1969 VW. I made just enough money selling my car to pay for food and gas on rideshare from Olympia, Washington back to New Alchemy.

The last stretch of my journey was a somewhat harrowing hitchhike, and I was relieved to arrive back at the New Alchemy gardens. While I was interested in the new crops being planted out, my eyes landed first on a guy with a long dark braid falling between his muscular shoulder blades. He was shoveling compost into a wheelbarrow without pause. "That's Ricky," said my friend and head gardener, Pete. "He can do that all day."

Ricky and I were both twenty-two. Our love blossomed over four seasons, with days spent sweating in the gardens and swims in Coonamessett Pond. Our love also met its challenging moments during nonmonogamous blips inspired by the vibrant energy of other young doers and seekers that thrived all around us. We loved each other, yet were both independent spirits on parallel journeys of our youth. I spent another year at New Alchemy helping to run the youth gardening programs by day and waited on tables full of tourists at the Fishmonger Cafe in Woods Hole by night. As per a plan with Marshall, who also had the farming and adventure bug, I emptied my coffee can stuffed with tips and bought a plane ticket. She and I spent a few months bicycling through England and France before I headed to the temples and peaks of India and Nepal while she followed her heart to Mali and a man named Seth who was in the Peace Corps there.

I returned from India ten months later with a yoga practice, many stories, and intestinal parasites. Ricky and I tried again but the timing was off. A painful breakup kept us apart but for a fleeting yet deep connection after spreading Jasper the dog's ashes under the mulberry tree. Ricky dove into work on his farm in the Ithaca area. I headed to Western Mass to pursue my interests in environmental education, and later multicultural education, working with great mentors at Antioch University New England (who accepted me without a bachelor's degree) and then UMass. I also found the teachers that would incite and support my studies of yoga and dance.

As I approached thirty, while in the midst of my doctoral work, a personal crisis had me make a short list of those in the world I loved and trusted the most. I wrote Ricky's name in the top five, then asked him to come visit. Ricky's farming partnership had ended and he was in Florida, rebuilding a friend's home after Hurricane Andrew and thinking about his next steps. He came. It was the right time.

## Our War Zone Honeymoon Tour

Our days through that summer of re-love were spent doing assorted work for money, fixing up my parents' future retirement house while living there, and growing a beautiful garden in the adjacent field. Mount Toby was the backdrop that awakened us at sunrise. Ricky began going to the nearby Leverett Peace Pagoda to offer his carpentry skills on the new temple the Japanese Buddhist monks and nuns were building—the first temple having succumbed to fire just months after its inauguration. We were married on Sept 17, 1994 at the edge of water gardens at

Young love and our first farm dog, Jasper.

the Peace Pagoda, witnessed by 200 friends and family who sat facing us on long wooden benches we had made for the occasion (and then left in place so the humble monks and nuns would have seating for future ceremonies!).

The sense of community at the Peace Pagoda was reminiscent of New Alchemy. Funky yet focused, socially and politically astute but with a strong spiritual core—aspects which were becoming increasingly important to us to merge with our lives as farmers. One day after working on the temple with others, Ricky heard the call of the drum as the monks and nuns were preparing for a ceremony. He felt the pull of an upcoming journey that the monks and nuns of Nipponzan Myohoji were planning in the tradition of their teacher Nichidatsu Fuji, as well as Gandhi, King, and others who practiced nonviolence and prayerful walk as a path towards peace. As we lay in the grass next to our garden at the end of that day, Ricky announced his intention to join the Interfaith Pilgrimage for Peace and Life that would traverse from Auschwitz to Hiroshima over the following year. "What about me?" I asked, pausing to consider my current situation, four years into a doctorate in multicultural education. Handing me a calendula he had just plucked from our garden, he asked that we marry and then go on the pilgrimage together. It would come to be an eight-month 'honeymoon' through some of the most intense places on the planet.

Our wedding was an eclectic affair. Our dear friend Phyllis Brown, African American scholar/goddess, presided. Buddhist chanting and Jewish elements honored our culture and our ancestors. Three months later, we were on our way to begin the International Interfaith Pilgrimage for Peace and Life from Auschwitz to Hiroshima. We knew that to witness so much suffering in the world would inform our lives, our marriage, and our direction forward.

We flew to Poland at the end of November 1994 having had just enough time to put together all the money we had, including some saved by cooking all the food ourselves for our wedding. Often working late into the night, I was able to crank out a draft of the first three chapters of my dissertation that I put on floppy disks and into a safe deposit box. Friends and family agreed to care for our beloved dogs Chico and Jackson. Leaving for the unknown, I wasn't sure I would ever finish my dissertation. I couldn't be sure that we'd even make it back alive. But we assured our family we absolutely would, that we were not joining a cult, and that we would make good choices for ourselves and out of our strong desire to have a future. With a roster that included walking through Gaza, Iraq, Bosnia, and Cambodia, we were not ignorant of what we were walking towards.

In JFK Airport, we met Marcus. The big drum he was carrying, sun-leathered skin, and relaxed vibe suggested he might be heading where we were. We introduced ourselves to the Australian, who was carrying the drum for American Indian Movement co-founder Dennis Banks to the convocation at Auschwitz. We were fast friends by the time we reached Krakow. We reunited with another friend upon arrival in Oswiecim, Poland, the village surrounding the horror of the Auschwitz concentration camp. We had already met Jhos, a brilliant musician, heavily tattooed lesbian (now a Trans Guy) and budding Jewish scholar from Berkeley at the Peace Pagoda earlier that fall. We would share a

ghost-filled room in a roughly converted building at the edge of Auschwitz during the convocation of interfaith peace leaders from around the world that preceded the walk; here we shared tears and made each other laugh—a necessity to make it through the days and months to come. Jhos and Marcus, as well as Souk from Thailand, Olga from Chile, Everardo from Costa Rica, and Vietnam veterans Claude and Billy would prove to be our closest friends of the fifty or so walkers that continued on from the convocation to the pilgrimage.

We prepared physically for walking twenty miles a day, but could not anticipate the depth of emotions through which we would journey. *Photo credit Billy Ledger.*

We walked through the coal-infused air of the grey Poland winter in the direction of the Czech Republic and on the same route of the death march that prisoners had been forced to walk by the Nazis just days before the liberation of the camps. We continued together for many months on this pilgrimage commemorating the 50th anniversary of the end of World War II and the beginning of the Cold and nuclear wars. Not your typical honeymoon, but a journey that we felt we had to make.

Given the eight months through twelve countries, and with about twenty miles a day on our feet plus some wild rides in between, there were plenty of stories made on the Pilgrimage. None of these involved a chaise lounge on a beach, or nights filled with lovemaking. In fact, every night pretty much involved laying down a bedroll in a place we never knew we'd be until we got there, then trying to sleep amid the scents and snores of fifty others. The most flesh we exposed to each other was our blistered feet in order to apply a new layer of moleskin before slipping them into a pair of dirty wool socks.

We got our first chance to be alone during a 'homestay' in the Czech Republic, about four weeks after walking through the cold and grey days of December. Hosts in each country had been pre-arranged by Sasamori, the esteemed monk who had initially envisioned this pilgrimage, to offer us whatever food and lodging might be possible. After walking all day, we would hastily drop our bags and head to a central community location for a meal and conversation in multiple languages with the locals. At the end of one such gathering, our host *du jour* said that there were some families who would welcome people into their homes if anyone wanted to do so, rather than lay out our sleeping bags on the church floor. Ricky and I looked at each other and quickly seized the opportunity. The Czech family had an old pull-out sofa in the living room of their small apartment. As quietly as possible, we made love that night. With the walking and changes of location each day knocking things off of any regular moon rhythm, I had no idea where I was in my menstrual cycle. When my period failed to arrive on time a few weeks later in Turkey, we began to consider what we would do. Seeking some semblance of humor we referred to the potential being as "Baby

Auschwitz Baklava" and considered what it would be like to be in Japan in my second trimester. This was not to happen as I did get my period. Even then, we knew it would have been very difficult to not keep a child conceived after paying witness to the genocide of our people.

By the time we had passed through Austria (where, in many places, we were keenly aware of lingering attitudes and manifestations of the Third Reich) and were approaching the former Yugoslavia, we knew we needed a break from the loveable yet dysfunctional group, but one that would be aligned with the spirit of the journey. We were not far from Turkey, land of my paternal family. My grandparents Letaru and Joseph, Sephardic Jews, had emigrated from Turkey to New York. My ancestors had been forced out during the Spanish Inquisition, and fled to Turkey, where they had since lived for 500 years. Auschwitz had surfaced a longing to connect to the Diaspora of our people, plus I had family there that I had never met.

Istanbul immediately wrapped us in and actually provided us with a true, unplanned honeymoon, as well as time to pursue another reason for joining the pilgrimage: a search for solidarity with other farmers throughout the world. We found a simple room in Sultanahmet, the Old City, and started our days of endless walking with a simple breakfast of simit bread piled in pyramid formation on trays balanced on the heads of street vendors. We ate fasuli beans, fish freshly fried on boats docked on the Bosphorus, and creamy rice pudding baked in clay pots. At the farmers' markets, we bought seeds of unique melons and beans, and then tucked them into our bags for return, starting our collection for the future Seeds of Solidarity gardens. We met my second cousins, who introduced us to all of the significant Sephardic locations in this city redolent of European and Asian elements.

We traveled to Cappadocia in Anatolia, wandering among homes and monasteries carved into the rocks left from volcanic deposits while we stayed at a tiny guesthouse with an elder farming family who served us fresh sheep cheese and apricot jam from their own trees. We hopped a bus to a fishing village on the coast, where we found ourselves in the only place to stay, a room rented by brothers who we surmised to be banned intellectuals with socialist, labor, or otherwise politically unpopular leanings. We drank tea in the smoke-filled cafe while men played backgammon with mind-bending speed and women cooked, cleaned, and tended the crops—a theme we would see repeated consistently in different landscapes throughout our travels.

We rejoined the pilgrimage in the Holy Land after the group had gone to (and fortunately made it out of) the former Yugoslavia, with fighting still happening in Bosnia at that time. We had strongly considered whether we should go on to Israel and Palestine given the bloody images of suicide bombings and checkpoint violence that were not censored from the TV behind the desk of the last cheap hotel we stayed at in Turkey. It felt important in many ways, though, so after unpacking our fears and repacking our bags we departed for Tel Aviv. Reunited with the monks, nuns, and our international friends now with another layer of callused blisters and stories, we walked throughout the lands of Palestine and Israel. Along the way, we met with leaders of the nonviolence movement on the West Bank and visited Neve Shalom, an educational community designed to unite Arab, Jewish, and Christian teenagers. We talked with a learned rabbi in a controversial settlement that spoke of sharing Torah teachings with an imam who, in turn, interpreted from the Koran.

We had a meal with the couple that would later publish the book *The Lemon Tree* about their reparation efforts after learning they lived in a home that had been taken from a Palestinian family. There were no home-stays here for us honeymooners and the uncertainty of political complexity filled the days and nights. On one of our last nights in Gaza, our group was led to a musty gym for our sleeping quarters, where we all unrolled our mats between archaic bench presses. There was no sweet candlelight. Instead, neon lights blared and hummed all night as our group gathered only a few minutes of sleep here and there, well aware of the machine-gun-strapped Palestinian soldier protecting us from whoever it was that we might need protection from as he chain-smoked in the doorway.

Over the next few months, the pilgrimage continued from Jordan to Iraq, Iraq to India, India to Malaysia, Malaysia to Thailand, and then to the border of Cambodia. India was ripe with all the scents and colors of life as I'd experienced there ten years prior, but this time with new awareness as we walked from village to village and united with another pilgrimage honoring the 125th birthday of Mahatma Gandhi. This increased our numbers, our energy, and our focus on the principle of ahimsa, nonviolence.

As we completed the India leg of the journey, a sudden two-week hiatus was created for our group upon learning that we would not be able to assemble and walk as planned in Singapore, due to their restrictions on assemblies of larger than twenty-five (for fear of uprising). And so we went off on another potential mini-honeymoon before reuniting with the group in Malaysia. But it would not be so. In the mountains of Manali in Northern India, Ricky would not get out of bed. He was sick with exhaustion and depression from what we had seen and where we had been, capped by the devastation and despair witnessed in Iraq. We finally found a Tibetan doctor who pointed to his head and provided some pills formed of local herbs that looked like rabbit scat and soon restored Ricky to balance.

As we walked through Malaysia and Thailand and prayed at sites that the Japanese had invaded and bombed, we directed our collective energy to witness and support the painful regret of the monks, nuns, and Japanese laypeople on the pilgrimage. Our time in Thailand was also rich with beauty as our group was invited to stay in an indigenous hill-tribe village as well as many wats, or Buddhist temples, including one deep in the jungle. It was here, at the border of Cambodia, where Ricky and I decided we would spend our last days with the pilgrimage group.

We were devoted to the cause of this journey, but increasingly uncomfortable with the lack of group communication and strategizing for emergency as we headed into some of the more dangerous terrain in Cambodia. Our commitment to our own lives and future as a newly married couple with many ideas and dreams took precedence. We said our goodbyes to the group, then spent a few more days with the nuns of this magical jungle wat, walking along with them as they gathered wild plants for our dinners together. From there, we continued on our own pilgrimage, spending a month in Vietnam—Saigon, the Mekong

Delta, and then finally, the Central Highlands. We walked, biked, and listened in order to learn all we could about the legacy left by the war on Vietnam, and the generation into which we were born. We had come of age in a society imprinted by the devastation of this war, and by the vital civil rights, feminist, and environmental movements that rose with great power around it. We added seeds of melons and squash from a farmers' market in the hills of Dalat, Vietnam to the others we had collected and stashed in our backpacks as we'd crossed many borders. It was time to return to familiar soil to make a garden and culminate our first year of marriage.

## *Looking for Land in all the Wrong Places*

After the good part of a year sleeping on a different musty floor every night, our desire to lay our heads on our own piece of land was strong. Transitioning back from the pilgrimage, we holed up at Deb's brother's house in New Hampshire, trying to acclimate to life in North America. Open to the right land at a price we could afford, we began poking around in rural New Hampshire (too many trucks with confederate flags), followed by visiting some spots for sale in Vermont (too many groovy white people), finally circling back into Massachusetts (some of both, and then some). We considered living in a more urban area, as neither of us had been brought up rural, and trying our hand at something like the Berkeley Integral Urban House that we had learned about while we were at New Alchemy.

We realized the general region in which we already lived offered a lot: forested and rural landscapes as well as small cities, an artistic culture, and a potential market for farm produce. Good solar exposure, fresh water for irrigation, and affordability were high on our list. Finally, a piece in Western Franklin County seemed promising: an old farmhouse nestled below a ridge of ample, albeit worn land. Then, after months of pursuit, we got the news that the estate lawyer left to deal with this piece we had been actively negotiating for four months was instead whittling away the trust money for his personal gain. The deal was going nowhere and it was time for us to let go. We had been looking for land almost full-time for eight months. While this was definitely a first-world, privileged problem, we were seriously bummed and, uncharacteristically, spent a weekend in bed—not joyfully, but moping with defeat.

We had been looking for pieces of land that were off of a realtor's radar, such as land under APR (agricultural preservation restriction) or a land trust, hoping this would help us find a unique place and with a price tag we could afford. We also fantasized some childless old farmer would think we were super cute and just pass on their parcel...but that didn't happen either. Our dear friends Micky and Samuel had made us members of an organization called Mount Grace Land Conservation Trust as a holiday gift. When Micky heard my voice so weepy and pathetic, she encouraged us to give the land trust director, Leigh Youngblood, a call. None of us could have known then that we would become the first farm-based project for this new organization which focused on forest protection.

We were in such a negative space when we made the call, it is amazing that Leigh actually wanted to keep talking to us. She told us about a piece in Orange that we might be interested in seeing. Testimony to the resilience of the spirit: one minute we were completely disillusioned, but with a new possibility on the horizon, off we went with renewed enthusiasm. While we were only living about twenty miles away, we never really had a reason to go east towards the town of Orange, so we knew nothing about this community as our work and friends had been oriented in other directions. As we soon learned upon hearing "Why would you want to move to Orange?" multiple times, negative perceptions of this struggling community resulted in a red line between the Five College Area and the poorer North Quabbin region. We found ourselves on Chestnut Hill Road, Orange, Massachusetts.

As the crow flies, it was not far from where we had been living in Montague. During our first six months on that land, we would traverse every possible road between the Montague and Orange multiple times, with tool-bags and thermos on the floor of the truck and two large dogs stuffed between us on the bench seat. On that first hopeful trip out, Deb realized she had been on the road before. There was a card still in her Rolodex for Bruce and Rachel, makers of Kallisti Marimbas, who lived at the end of the road where she'd picked hers up years before. Driving down it for the second time, we didn't yet know that this dirt road would be the seasonally snowy, muddy, and verdant vein of our life to come.

Because our primary interest was farming, most of the land we had looked at consisted of open fields. But the piece we now approached was not an open field. A patchwork of small and overgrown fields was intermingled with forested areas and *a lot* of rocks. Spring-fed wetlands sloping to the east left the land pretty wet, and ample laurel suggested acidic soil. While it didn't look anything like the expanses of fields we had previously considered that called out 'farming,' this was a compelling spot with a lot of history, including rock walls and an old stone foundation.

A narrow path led to a small clearing in the forest, with signs of logging thirty or so years back—lots of stumps and an old skidder tire but not much else. With Leigh, we wandered the snow-dusted February fields with a shovel, tape measure, and compass. We used the compass to check out solar access, and dug a few small holes into the cold earth to try to get a sense of the soil type. We'd envisioned building a home in a private, wooded spot with good solar access. It was long abandoned and undeveloped, with no rich river bottom loam and, in fact, no farm-worthy soil at all. But we were at peace with that and open to the challenge. It felt right.

Many years later, at one of our Solidarity Saturday farm tour traditional opening circles, neighbors Jeff and Shali shared that, before we bought the land, they used to walk that narrow path to the small clearing where we would come to build our homestead and greenhouses. There they would look up at the stars and call in the aliens. We laughed. The call was answered and here we were: two Ashkenazi Sephardic Jews landing on Turtle Island, original land of the Nipmuc People, here to try our best to live close to the earth and grow some food.

## *Encounters with a Preservation Imperialist*

Nobody introduced the odd man out at the table when we went to have
our first serious meeting about purchasing the land on Chestnut Hill
Road. He was a thin white guy who looked to be about seventy, and sat
next to the regional director from Mass Audubon. His old flannel shirt
and khakis clothed him like a humble birdwatcher, but I got a strange
vibe. We were too nervous with excitement and land negotiation inex-
perience to come right out and ask who he was and what he was doing
at the table.

As we'd soon come to find out after asking around, Simon was
the local bankroller for Mass Audubon and other land conservation
projects. The signs we'd noticed around the forests that read "Protected
lands: no entry without permit; no dogs, hunting, fishing" were largely
his doing. Frankly, we would have much preferred a dude from New
Jersey in a suit blatantly flashing his roll of hundreds. But the silent
New England Puritan vibe he exuded was less familiar and gave us the
creeps. Over a few more meetings, what some might call strong pres-
ervationist values, and others might call classism, became apparent.
While not an insurmountable issue to the completion of the land deal,
it added a veil of discomfort to the process throughout.

We never negotiated with Simon directly. He was buying the land
across from and behind ours, and then donating a conservation restriction on those parcels to Mass Audubon on which he would hang more
of those signs. We were dealing directly with Mount Grace and that
relationship was relatively agreeable. We were experienced enough to
realize we were inexperienced, though, and made the smart move to
hire a local lawyer to help us negotiate. Simon's purchase of the adjacent parcels would help make the whole deal fly. Mount Grace, then a
small organization trying to gain capacity as well as protect as much
land as possible, was understandably well aware of this. One of Simon's
insistences was that a wildlife corridor be designated through the properties in question, including ours—a strip of land that would never be
touched or altered for any reason. We had no problem with creating
and supporting habitat, but the corridor proposal that restricted over

a quarter of the land seemed excessive. In fact, I asked a colleague at Antioch New England, where I taught environmental education, if it made sense to him. This well-respected conservationist concurred that a flexible zone considering how streams change over time would probably make more ecological sense. But flexibility was not part of Simon's communication. The negotiations became increasingly unpleasant.

The development of a Conservation Restriction (CR) involves thinking ahead in order to put into language all activities that might possibly occur on a piece of land over time. Over the course of six months, we carried out the essentials. Wetlands delineations and perc tests were done. We negotiated agreements for home, farm, and education program structures on the thirty-acre piece of property. We also proposed something for which we will always be grateful to our wonderful lawyer Pam for suggesting. Given that we were about to put all of our money on the table and commit to many years of hard work, we traded the back fifty wooded acres of the existing parcel that we didn't need (or want to pay taxes on, knowing that Simon and Mass Audubon would buy and protect it anyway) for an additional residential envelope at the far end of the property. We would be able to sell or build on that if we were ever strapped for cash, or wanted to gift it to a not-yet-born kid, or build a more accessible house for ourselves close to the road when we got old.

After nine months of negotiations, we were almost there and the last step seemed simple. There was a small wetland area along what would become a farm road to our future house. As part of that exercise in thinking ahead about everything in a CR, we proposed language to include some small benches for nature observation to be enjoyed by visitors. Soon after, Leigh called to convey a message from Simon that he would give us $500 to take the observation bench out of the CR draft. I'd had it with this mystery moneyman and was now maximumly insulted by the accumulation of his patronizing comments, and tired of the endless negotiations. I lost it on the phone and provided a brief yet graphic description of what he could do with those five bills. Regretfully, we once again thought we might have to let go of another piece of land, but at least would do so with vision and pride intact. Leigh obviously did not quote me directly, and apparently handled it with more grace than I could muster. Our wetland bench idea stayed. And importantly, we closed the deal on what would become Seeds of Solidarity Farm and Education Center.

We saw Simon a few times after that, passing him in his dented, blue Honda on the road, or seeing him in the distance, unwinding a long roll of string to measure up his next land project. A simple wave felt fine, and there was little emotional charge behind it. The frustration we had felt faded into the background once we had signed the papers and started building our home and nourishing the soil for crops. Eventually we learned that his time had come. Certainly, his legacy left good things and his own dream fulfilled. Around the area, one can still see many of the "no entry" signs he tacked to trees here and there on the many acres he bought, often shot up a bit by hunters perhaps also pissed off at the tone of exclusion—or maybe just for target practice. Given grave environmental and justice issues of fracking and coal mining, large hydro replacing small communities in the Global South, the contamination of the food supply and climate change, the small things like preservation politics matter less. But questions lingered: who has the right to own and control land—land stolen from indigenous people in the first place? And how could we respect the land as sacred, steward it well, and generate a livelihood while keeping it accessible to many?

## *Breaking Ground, Making Home*

We celebrated the closing on our land two days after Christmas, 1996, with margaritas in a basement bar. Along with a mortgage, we had also crafted a conservation restriction over the course of nine months of negotiations. This document of perpetuity described a residential envelope where we would build our house, any number of greenhouses and agricultural buildings, woodlot for firewood and some lumber, and structures for educational programs. We didn't know exactly what would go where or when, but we were itching to go. Our agreement with the sellers, Mount Grace Land Conservation Trust, enabled us to begin some light work on the land that fall as the paperwork was being finalized. Before winter set in, we needed to hand-dig holes and pour six foundation piers for our first building, a 12-by-24-foot toolshed that would also function as an outdoor kitchen. We had figured that if the whole thing fell through, the most we would have lost would be some scythed land and the concrete we hauled in by wheelbarrow for the piers. If it all worked, we'd have something to build on before the earth froze solid.

The day after the closing we filled the cab of the old Nissan pickup truck like an ark: two large dogs, two cheese sandwiches, two thermos of hot tea, and the two of us. We were swaddled in Carhartt insulated work suits and the truck bed was filled with tools. Just before the New Year, Ricky's buddy Earle had showed up from Ithaca in his usual good and generous spirits. His energetic arrival propelled us past the six concrete piers to some initial framing, giving the first of our buildings form. We had no electricity on the site so we charged our 18-volt cordless driver and saw in the truck lighter during our midday break, using that time to warm our frigid hands over a scrap wood fire in a 55-gallon metal barrel. Our dogs Chico and Jackson scouted the woods. This routine continued everyday through February as we framed what we came to call 'the little house.' We had first imagined a simple outdoor kitchen and tool storage, but quickly realized it would likely take us two or three years of time and money-making at other jobs to build a house. Had we had the foresight, we could have coined the term tiny-house and made some money doing a reality show while we were still young and pretty.

Ricky's years working as a builder during farming off-season guided our construction as we worked away. At that time, the 700-foot path down to the clearing was, well, still a path—as opposed to the rut-filled 'upgraded' driveway that it is now. Needing to reserve our funds for building materials rather than driveway grading and gravel, we hoisted two by sixes on our shoulders and filled wheelbarrows with tools and bales of recycled cotton insulation, and hiked it all in, day by day.

Ricky worked on the cottage most days, while I put my doctorate to work and taught a few classes in the Environmental Studies department at Antioch University New England in Keene. I taught by day, then donned black pants and dress shirt to wait tables at the newly opened Blue Heron Restaurant in the evenings. This kept some bucks for building materials and basic expenses trickling in, and created some healthy space so we were happy to see each other at the end of those few but long days and nights apart. We also remained involved with a cultural identity afterschool program in Northampton where we taught with a fabulous, diverse group of co-facilitators (and lasting friends) who would later help bless our new home with a meal on a table made of plywood that filled the entirety of our small cottage's interior.

Our plan was that we would frame, insulate, and sheetrock the one-room cottage. By late spring we would upgrade the driveway sufficiently to drive in the large windows we'd bought (recycled from an

 old school) and accommodate a concrete truck so we could pour a slab floor around the piers and up to the walls. One of our favorite construction photos is of ourselves at 3:00 A.M. Taken by a remote with the camera balanced on the hood of the truck, the flash il-

Doing what it takes.

luminates our hands and faces smeared in dark-red pigmented concrete as we stayed up through the night to hourly trowel the wet concrete floor smooth.

By spring, the cottage was camp-style livable, with an outdoor burner and sink for cooking and washing dishes. We moved our modest possessions over from my parent's house in Montague. Fortunately, we hadn't alienated all of our

While building the little house, we started in on the site for the main house, clearing some brush and pounding in scrap wood to mark the corners.

friends during our almost singular focus on finding land. We invited a few of the particularly building-talented and artsy ones over to help stucco the exterior, followed by a feast of hot soup and bread outside our cozy nest of a little home in the forest. This theme would repeat a few more times over the coming years as we built and readied frames for two stories of the main house and lifted them into place with friends and neighbors during what we referred to as our 'Jewish-Amish wall-raising parties.'

We had decided on the land for its affordability and potential without really knowing anything about the town of Orange. When we first drove through town to find our way to the lumberyard that we would frequent, the boarded up storefronts, preponderance of liquor stores, and teenagers pushing their baby carriages did not exactly paint a picture of a vibrant community. But then we began to meet our new neighbors on Chestnut Hill Road.

Lydia was the first. She warmly invited us over on one of the weekends we spent scything to see what the land might hold, before we had fully formalized the land purchase. Her invitation for a salmon dinner with wine was a wonderful reprieve from those cheese sandwich lunches followed by hasty dinners back in Montague after long days of working. After dinner we visited her studio to see her sculptural pottery, which would become increasingly beautiful and bold as her marriage ended. Lydia was to become one of our closest friends and co-visionary/founder of the North Quabbin Garlic and Arts Festival.

During that first winter of building, another neighbor—one directly across the street—invited us in for tea and cookies, which we could not resist. This became a regular ritual when she saw us looking particularly frozen. She talked and talked as we just listened, thankful for twenty minutes in a warm house with tea that hadn't cooled to tepid in a thermos. She moved out, but her husband remained and has been an ever-supportive neighbor. An organ builder by trade, Stefan's understanding of all things circuitry would later grow into a solar installation business. His recycled oil furnace and smokers for home-raised pork added to the air of invention on Chestnut Hill Road. As we built, other neighbors began to stop by: Bruce and Doug kidnapped us for lunch one day—perhaps to grill us on our intentions as they were the long-term homesteaders and house-husbands on the hill. They would later show up for all of our wall-raisings with their wives Rachel and Sally, and become good friends and fine partying partners.

We had bought land with no knowledge of the community, but fortuitously found ourselves among some amazingly resourceful neighbors who never complained about the stream of farm apprentices, van loads of youth for our program for local teens, truckloads of cardboard unloaded to mulch our fields, and a plethora of other sometimes insane (and always experimental) ideas. This proved more important and nurturing than we could have ever imagined. Now, when visitors ask if we ever considered living 'in community' (by which they mean an intentional community), we reply that we do: it is called a neighborhood. We knew we had more than our work cut out for us to build a homestead, transform barren land into a farm, fulfill our educational vision, and figure out how to earn a livelihood and raise a family. It appeared our spaceship had landed in the right place.

## *Field Guide: Journey of a Self-Created Life*

### Questions to Ponder: Vision and Lifestyle

- Articulate some of the values that are important to you. These might relate to physical, spiritual, or emotional ways of being or seeing. Is there alignment or conflict among these and your current relationships, work, lifestyle, and the place you live?

- What is something you would change in the short term and in the long term to increase alignment between your values and lifestyle?

- What is a personal vision you have brought to fruition in the past? What factors made this exciting and successful?

- Just to free your mind, if you were able to remove real or perceived constraints (e.g. money, fear), what is a dream you'd love to bring to fruition?

## Down to Earth: *Do It Yourself*

### *Create a Value-Based Vision Plan*

Whether you are building a house, starting a small farm, launching a food enterprise, or forming a group or organization, it is valuable to create goals both for the short term and longer term. A lot of people talk about the importance of a business plan, but skip the foundation of identifying and sharing core values. A sole focus on numbers can create stress and overshadow the spirit of your initial dream. It is important to articulate goals and a timeline, but these should reflect and emanate from your values, passion, and vision. A set of values may shift or grow, but they are a critical baseline. As you make decisions along the way, you can refer back to ensure your actions are harmonious with these values.

This process assumes you will be sharing this planning with someone else—a partner, friend, colleague, or small discussion group. It can be done in one long sitting with breaks—such as a half-day retreat together—or broken up over several conversations.

1) Individually, each person generates two lists. The first list is **qualities** of life you feel you currently embody or emanate that inspire passion and purpose. The second is qualities that you would like to evolve. Use words, symbols, or pictures to reflect these. Such qualities might include optimism, balance, diligence, humor, flexibility, open-mindedness, listening, honesty, and creativity. Share your lists with each other in the spirit of active listening and mutual support. This gives a sense of what you personally bring or wish to bring to an initiative.

2) It may be that you are using this process for an existing idea—such as the creation of a task force or building a home or community greenhouse. Or perhaps you are at a point in your life where you want to generate something new and yet unknown.

Regardless, generate a list of current or desired **values** individually or in conversation (values might include qualities, but are often broader and reflect a worldview or principles). Such values might include racial justice, reverence for the land, spirituality, simplicity, self-sufficiency or collaboration. Be real rather than feel the need to list everything possible. Less is often more.

3) Consider both the desired qualities and values you generated in relation to an existing project or vision. Or, if there is nothing specific on the table, what is a possible idea or direction that embodies your current or aspirational values? On your own, with a partner, or as a small group, draft and share a **vision statement** that reflects these qualities and values. You can stop here for now, or...

4) You can now decide how far you want to look into the future. It may be one year (short term), or three to five years (longer term). With the lists of qualities and values and the vision statement you drafted as your guides, forge up to three concrete short- and/or long-term **goals** aligned with your vision statement. Be gentle and realistic so you don't try to overachieve and then get discouraged. As you do this, you may refine your vision statement, too, or generate a few more qualities and values. You might also find that one vision statement is too broad and is asking to be broken into smaller, manageable pieces. Write or draw what you have conjured in a beautiful way so that you can contemplate and enjoy it and let it all simmer towards action.

## Awaken The Power: *Contemplative Practice*

### *Your Resilience Toolbox*

This book offers stories and inspiration for an engaged life. In order to achieve that, tools for contemplation and resilience are necessary. We must develop healthy ways to re-center and balance so that we have the strength to continue to give to others, be present in a multitude of situations, and be better partners, friends, and parents. We cultivate this resilience through good and hard times. As we move through life, we can gather tools for our resilience toolbox that support both self-care and our ability to be of service by sharing these tools. A multitude of contemplative, creative, and healing practices and modalities support resilience.

Consider what you currently do for rejuvenation, to rid yourself of swirling thoughts, or to ease stress naturally. These might include meditation, yoga, dance, journaling, crafts, walks in nature, reading, cooking, making or listening to music, martial arts, tai chi, massage, or soothing teas and flower essences. Or, you might not yet have anything in your toolbox. Perhaps one of these ideas appeals to you; most require no or little money to continue once learned. What is one contemplative practice that appeals to you, or that you want to rededicate yourself to? What are the (real or imagined) barriers that keep you from incorporating a contemplative practice in your life with consistency? Time? Anxiety? A dedicated space? Resources? Teachers? Start with one that doesn't require much time, energy, or resources. These might include: breathing slowly, taking a silent walk, sipping tea slowly, some simple stretches, or reading a poem. Pick one that you commit to do each day for two weeks, even for just five minutes a day. It might be helpful to embark on this with someone else so you can share your experiences. After two weeks either continue or try another practice. Whatever happens, you will have contributed to your resilience toolbox.

## Ten Ways to Keep Your Vision Real

1. Check in with yourself often.
2. Check in with your partner informally and through meetings.
3. Seek friends or mentors to help you evolve your vision—and you, theirs.
4. Set times for in-depth reflection on past goals and for envisioning new ones, perhaps seasonally or twice a year.
5. Stay inspired by others through books and videos to keep your vision fresh and informed.
6. Meditate, pray, journal—whatever works for you—to stay centered and focused.

7. Ask your guides, the universe, God—whoever you connect with on that realm—for guidance.

8. Attend to changing needs and changing times and adjust your vision accordingly.

9. Let go of goals or ideas that didn't work out, serve the big picture, or are no longer relevant in order to make space for new ones.

10. Use creativity to bring out subtleties in your vision.

*Chapter Two*

# Grow Food Everywhere: Farming for Life

## *Not Your Typical Farm*

I finish the breakfast dishes with just enough time to greet the folks arriving for one of our Solidarity Saturday farm tours as Deb sets up a folding table for the potluck lunch that will follow. We never know who will show up, but offer this day to open our farm to the public and share our ways of working with the land. Two decades after we first walked our land, what remains obvious to any visitor is that Seeds of Solidarity is not your typical farm. There are no large expanses of flat fields or muddy tractors. Instead, they witness a landscape of small fields surrounded by woods and wetlands, sloping towards our home and outbuildings, which are enveloped by a patchwork of gardens and greenhouses. Many thousands of visitors—seasoned farmers, sustainable agriculture students, urban gardeners, old-time locals, young back-to-the landers—have come to see how we have been able to transform barren land into an abundant oasis, and take some ideas back to their own communities. We are always sure to remind them that what they see evolved over many years with a lot of creativity and resourcefulness, and, importantly, that there is not any one way to do anything—this is but our vision and intention put into one form.

When we were first negotiating with Mount Grace Land Conservation Trust, it got back to us that a board member had said, "They will never be able to grow anything on that land." That sparked our energy even more. Instead of purchasing a turnkey farm and fields (which we couldn't afford anyway), we were motivated to make a farm work on this land that would be a model for others. At the beginning of a farm tour, we often ask the group where the best soil in our region might be. The answer? Under thirty-eight square miles of water called the Quabbin

Reservoir, previously a valley of four vibrant agricultural communities seized by eminent domain in the late 1930s to flood in order to supply Boston with drinking water.

Our land was just above that valley. Like most New England land, it was historically forested, inhabited by indigenous peoples (in our case, the Nipmuc), then stolen and cleared by 'settlers' who grazed sheep. Our land holds a story of a family whose father left to fight in the Civil War, leaving his wife and daughters to sustain family life and peach trees while living in a house on what is now Chestnut Hill Road. Old stone foundations from a barn and carriage house remain. When we arrived, the land had not been cultivated since then—and never for crops. Small, overgrown fields interspersed in the rocky forest had thin to no topsoil. One had some semi-decent growing soil from grazing years ago. Others were quite wet. Abundant laurel indicated high acidity. No, this was certainly not a turnkey operation. In fact, it would have been harder to find a more difficult site for a vegetable farm. If we could find a way to grow food on this land, it could happen almost anywhere.

Our priority: build the first greenhouse before the main house! With a small crew composed of a pregnant wife and his parents offering advice, Ricky framed the walls on the newly poured slab to lift with the help of neighbors later.

We had rough ground, no buildings or power, no pond for irrigation, and no existing market. We did have a decade of experience growing food and a lot of energy and determination. We would need it.

Soon after we built the cottage, we erected our first greenhouse: a forty-foot hoop house next to the spot where the foundation for the main house would go. Looking around, I wondered how we would possibly begin to work with the land. We had no money for labor or machinery and I had no desire to use that machinery after a decade of doing so at my previous farm in New York. Overflowing dumpsters of corrugated cardboard caught my eye. Whenever we drove the fifteen miles from Deb's parent's house in Montague to Orange we would load up with cardboard from the recycling dumpster at the Leverett Village Food Co-op halfway between. We started on the field with the most promising soil (which wasn't saying much), layering cardboard onto the tall grasses and spreading mulch hay on top to hold down the cardboard. We expanded the area dumpster trip by dumpster trip throughout our first winter and early spring on the land. The grasses broke down under the cardboard and the ground underneath was ready to experience its first growing season. The weeds and sod had decomposed, and I figured there was decent enough soil to add some compost and see what might happen with some crops.

Meanwhile, down the path in the stump-filled clearing where we were building, there was absolutely no soil to work with at all and no grasses to cover with cardboard to add biomass. Off we went to some local farms where we loaded up the truck by hand with free or cheap aged manure. We put cardboard over the barren land, then unloaded the aged manure right on top to form a few 3½-by-75-foot beds, working in and around the stumps left by logging decades before. Day after day we layered cardboard. We then brought in manure and quality compost from various farms, building beds shovelful by shovelful while simultaneously building relationships with those farmers. We called it the 'insta-bed' method, and planted these with fast-growing salad greens as soon as the beds were made. Salad greens were a popular, fast-growing crop with shallow roots that could be broadcast, or 'scatter-sown,' on just four to six inches of nitrogen-rich soil. The only problem was water.

We didn't have a well, let alone any electricity to pump water out even if we had. Looking back, we realize that there were a few great blessings and alignments that sometimes made it seem like a higher power was looking out for us. We had first seen the land in winter, but with the thaw of the seasons we discovered several natural, clear springs coming down Chestnut Hill. One surfaced just across the road. Ah, if only we could access it. While we were walking down our dirt road one day, the town road crew passed by and asked if we minded if they put in a culvert under the road to channel the flowing springs. The issue was that it would flow onto our property. Well shit, sure! It would have cost us ample paperwork and perhaps thousands of dollars to try to get town permission for and then build this ourselves.

We had a lot of food grade barrels at the time that we had salvaged from a pickle factory. We cut some in half to serve as large container gardens for salad greens in the hoop house. We placed a half pickle barrel with plumbing fittings on our side of the culvert to gather the flowing water, out of which two-inch PVC pipe traveled a gradual downhill 1,000 feet towards our new greenhouse and insta-beds. We collected this light flow at the bottom of the hill, but it wasn't until a good rain came that there was enough pressure to water directly with a hose. When I heard a good rain (generally a summer thunderstorm at night), I would jump out of bed to soak the greenhouse and salad greens as Deb groggily requested that I not get struck with lightning. Baby Levi was in the mix now, too, and becoming a widowed mother was not in our five-year plan. With enough rain, four weeks after making and planting beds, the greens were ready. We were growing and delivering salad greens to some of the finest restaurants in the Pioneer Valley where diners unknowingly ate insta-bed salads grown by some of the craziest and most determined farmers imaginable.

Since we had been market gardening previously on a half-acre at Deb's parents place in Montague, we had some previous connections to great chefs and restaurants to our west and south in the Valley. These restaurants did not exist in Orange. We maintained our focus on growing mesclun salads and baby greens that didn't need deep soil. That was what the restaurants, co-ops and customers were newly craving. These early techniques and a steady market gave us time to build the soil and expand fields for a variety of other crops, but salad greens would remain our niche.

As the gardens began to expand to the edges of the logged area, and our need for greenhouses to extend the season and protect tender crops from weather extremes increased, we cut back the sapling regrowth on the forest edges to expand the perimeter of the clearing, which by now held the foundation for our main house, too. We had a deep well drilled in a promising spot located with the help of a fifth-generation water dowser. We initially hand-pumped water for crops and consumption. After three years, we installed the first phase of our solar electric system that pumped the sweet artesian water for home and farm—what a gift! We hired our friend and large equipment operator extraordinaire Rick Chafee to help us push the edges of the small clearing back and let in a little more sun. The downed trees became our firewood, and we brought in some sand to level an area for more hoop houses. Over the next five or six years, we put up four 30-by-96-foot greenhouses. There were many large rocks to move before pounding in ground-posts. We worked in blizzards. Early farm apprentices were also part of this process. To create fertile land within the hoop houses in order to start actually making money, we added a base of aged manure to the sand foundation, formed seven long raised beds about three and a half feet wide (with paths between just wide enough to walk with a wheelbarrow), then topped the beds with high quality finished compost from our friends at Diemand Farm. With the beds ready to plant, we sowed a diverse array of salad greens for market. Carpets of green hues were planted and harvested in succession through spring, summer, and fall. As we built the farm, we simultaneously began the first of many education programs to come: our SOL (Seeds of Leadership) Garden program for local teens. We devoted a small field at the far end of our property to this purpose, and used the same techniques there to nourish the soil along with young hearts and minds.

By this time, about five years of being a farm, we were friends with other local farmers who had composted manure, and we had a little more cash from selling our crops to pay them to dump truckloads.

What we started with.

We'd also made friends with the owner and workers at the local furniture business, who saved and stacked cardboard we continued to layer on the fields. They were able to save on their costs of hauling it out, and the workers were happy for the invitation to hunt on our land in exchange for delivery. Our land had been blanketed by a lot of La-Z-Boy recliner boxes, but the worms and microbes were anything but lazy as they churned through boxes, leaving more fertile soil in their wake. We didn't yet have much time for any reclining ourselves—but that was in our dreams, along with many other hopes and plans.

## Homage to my Early Farming Days: Tony the Godfather and Macrobiotic MacDonalds

The three years I spent apprenticing at the New Alchemy Institute in my early twenties were some of the most exciting of my life. It was a period rich with gained skills, inspiration, and a strong foundation from one of the first places in the world to research organic agriculture, aquaculture, and bioshelter design. I left when the time was right to head off into the world again to follow the dream that was now in my heart: starting my own farm. My close friend Stuart and I drove off in my old orange Toyota to look for land. Stuart had been a student in the college semester program at NAI and we had become good friends. We traveled through a few states and ended up purchasing a farm in upstate New York: ninety-six tillable acres, a magnificent barn, and a farmhouse for $86,000. Owner-financed, we would be able to pay it off month-by-month for something equivalent to rent. To support our own farming start-up, Stuart found work at a dairy farm and I did carpentry work. We were twenty-four years old, and becoming the proud owners of Jasper's Farm (named after the dog Deb and I had who was hit by a car at a too-early age, and whose ashes were buried under the giant mulberry tree at New Alchemy).

It was 1986 and the early years of organic farming and modern day 'local food' awareness (notwithstanding peoples throughout the world who never stopped growing and eating this way). Consumers were enthusiastically starting to seek our food. The USDA was still laughing at us, not taking the market or movement seriously. There were many wonderful growers in the area as Ithaca, New York was just

About eight years later.

seventeen miles south. It was right about the time that the idea of the CSA (community-supported agriculture) was arriving from Europe and only just starting to root, and before farmer's markets had sprung up like weeds. Small farmers needed to unite to create our markets. Finger Lakes Organic Growers, a new marketing cooperative, was just starting up and we joined on. We grew a wide selection of organic produce on seventeen acres, selling at the Ithaca Farmers Market, New York City Greenmarkets, and wholesale through Finger Lake Organics.

Mentors would be pivotal to my becoming a farmer, and to my way of learning throughout life. At New Alchemy, my farming mentor had been Johnny Rapoza, an old-time Portuguese potato grower who lived a few miles away, and who loved pesticides as much as his red wine. I bicycled over weekly to visit with Johnny and hear his life stories. Now in the Finger Lakes region, I got to know one of the early pioneers of organic farming, Tony Potenza, who we referred to as "The Godfather of Organic." He was an amazing vegetable grower, and he grew hundreds of acres of soybeans for a local tofu company. My new farming mentor was a charismatic Italian organic cowboy who loved his tractor and knew how to live life. Tony had soul and was (still is!) a colorful character. Everyone had a story about Tony. Some were good, some not so good. When we first arrived on the scene, Tony was still working on his second marriage, but most of the years I was there he was a bachelor and known as quite the playboy. Tony was also famous for Italian greens, selling what most considered weeds as exotic salad. He had a friend, a gay guy named Hitch, who would gather the wild greens to peddle with gusto at the market. I would visit Tony by night during the winter and sit by his woodstove as he shared farming stories. That was how the mentorship began.

Another well-known farming team at the time was the MacDonald family, made up of Tom, Shelley, and their six kids. It was through them I learned the term 'home-schooled.' All of their kids worked the farm. Rather than the quintessential farmhouse, barn, and field, the MacDonalds had built an apartment in their metal barn where they lived, using a former milk bulk tank cut to make a wood fired hot tub. Their place was one long room with Tom and Shelley's bed, a kitchen, living room, and little cubicle like rooms built for all the kids throughout the barn. They were authentic hippie back-to-the-land folks who loved to dance and party. The MacDonalds were macrobiotic and specialized in root crops and cucumbers for their famous lacto-fermented pickles before anyone but Koreans and the early students of Michio Kushi were seeking these. They were the first folks I knew of who went down to the Greenmarket in New York City, selling at the famous Union Square Market. With their fermented pickles, kimchi, and wheat-free baked goods they were at least twenty-five years ahead of the curve. It seemed I picked my teachers from folks living on the edge. Tony Potenza and the MacDonalds fit the bill. These folks were legends in their community. I was welcomed into their lives and continued to meet other Trumansburg and Ithaca characters: hippies, artists, and Vietnam vets that worked with their hands.

I stayed in the Ithaca area until I was twenty-nine, farming for three full seasons and doing carpentry for cash each winter. There were many stories of my own now to complement those collected from mentors. I'll always remember our second year farming. We had a good three weeks' worth of crops in the ground in black plastic, growing well. Then a major hailstorm arrived, and three weeks of work was immediately wiped away. I remember another time when, having driven through the night to a Greenmarket in NYC, it proceeded to rain all day. We didn't sell much, so, before heading north, we drove our truck over to Greenwich Village and offered up paper bags full of vegetables out of the back for twenty bucks a bag, clearing out most of our produce in the process. I learned a lot about marketing that day. While people may scoff at a three-dollar bunch of broccoli, give them a deal and they'll end up paying the same or more!

My relationship with Stuart started going south around our fourth year of farming together. As two guys farming together, living together, and basically doing most everything together, some folks assumed we were a couple, though neither of us swung that way. I had started to build my own small house on the land to begin to separate our lives a bit. But as the stress of farming waxed over time, Stuart became increasingly manic and violent in his ways. He began to lose it more and more often, screaming at neighbors and even physically threatening some people. With things going bad with Stuart, and the town starting to feel too small (everyone knew my business), it became clear that it was time to move on. Hurricane Andrew had just hit the southeast and a friend of a friend wanted to hire my best buddy Earle and me to rebuild his home in storm-devastated Homestead, Florida. The six years in Interlaken had been good. I was sad to leave my friends and partially framed house, but relieved to separate from my farming partner. I left with a lot more farming experience, a carpentry trade, and a good deal of stories from some great mentors—experiences that would help me be a mentor to many.

## Sorry I Can't Finish the Season, I'm in Jail

A couple of years into starting Seeds of Solidarity, we began to bring on farm apprentices two at a time for a six-month season. Throughout over a decade of working with apprentices, we hosted all sorts: serious farmer hopefuls and serial dramas, poets and roller derby players, vegans and voracious learners, meditators, and just one or two mistakes.

We'd had apprentices for each of the three seasons prior by the time Matt and Gloria arrived from Missouri. We also had interns who worked specifically with our budding education programs (but did not live on site). We had gotten to know some great young people as we literally grew the farm and our newly minted nonprofit while mentoring them. This encounter, though, would go on the record as the last time we agreed to farm apprentices via phone and references without actually meeting them.

I had dinner ready for them when they arrived late that April night. Although we were still in the early years of Seeds of Solidarity, we had already had many people around our big kitchen table where conversation and laughter usually flowed with ease. Not that night. Nothing flowed easily, nor the next morning when Gloria presented a list of "40 things wrong with the cottage" that had been our beloved first home and in which we now hosted apprentices: needs curtains, the ladder to the loft is too steep, we can't use our George Foreman Grill with the solar electric system, and so on.

As our friend Dan says, sometimes things start out good and go bad; sometimes they start out bad and get good. And sometimes, they go from bad to worse—which is exactly what happened. Matt and Gloria would show up every morning dour-faced. Gloria always had a hydration pack strapped to her back, and for what I don't know as she basically refused to do any significant work. Matt was silent and eerie-looking and followed her lead. Ricky managed to find them assorted 'assemble this' or 'paint that' projects to get them out of the way. They weren't much good in the field. And I saw her kick my dog once. We tentatively approached the idea of asking them to leave after they had been with us a couple of months, but they wanted to stay and we did not assert otherwise. I'm still not sure why we toughed it out—perhaps we were just trying to keep everything else together, and so pretended it wasn't as bad as it truly was.

We were resting up on a rainy Sunday morning in early August, with Ricky lying on our living room floor trying to get the intense spasms in his back to subside as I played with our toddler. Ricky had spent days hauling heavy crates of garlic balanced on one shoulder up two ladders to the unfinished third floor of our house and out of the moist air that had prevailed that August and was threatening to destroy the entire crop. Matt and Gloria knocked, came in, and said they thought it was time to go. I dug below my months of stored anger and frustration and mustered something to the effect of "We've all tried our best to make this work. We understand and hope you have a good life." Our somewhat shocked relief was palpable when their packed van drove off for the last time.

Ricky got some bodywork from a neighbor who mostly worked on thoroughbred horses, (so he knew how to get into those farmer muscles!). Fortunately, a friend's son had recently showed up in the midst of some life wandering and searching. He had a positive attitude and was willing to lend a hand in exchange for lunch and an occasional place to crash. We completed the garlic harvest and recalibrated for the remainder of season, relatively unscathed.

After that experience, we always met incoming apprentices in person before bringing them on, a process which we found to be much more illuminating than just a recommendation or resume. It became immediately clear which responses to our call for apprentices were canned and which were sincerely interested in our philosophy and methods. If a subsequent phone conversation moved the energy forward for them and for us, we set a date for an in-person interview. This interview came to include our "Ernest Shackleton Endurance Test" wherein prospective apprentices were offered tea and conversation around the kitchen table to test for ease and laughter, then led into some slightly outrageous project like helping put the skin on a greenhouse amidst February snowbanks to see if they approached tasks with enthusiasm or dismay. With this method we gained some very hearty and enjoyable apprentices who infused the fabric of the farm with wonderful energy and more wild stories. And, as with any carefully thought-through process, sometimes good people arrive—and leave—in unexpected ways, as happened with one apprentice who we will call Linus.

We didn't think too much of it when we heard Linus' van return at 3:00 a.m. late one Sunday after his weekend off. Most of our apprentices were in their mid- to late twenties so we'd seen plenty of the exploration and personal drama that can come with those years. While the majority of our farm apprentices were good to go every morning, we'd also started days with tears on our shoulders from a breakup with the perpetually bad boyfriend, or the occasional bleary eyes hidden behind sunglasses after a night of drinking. But when Linus told us he couldn't finish out the season because he had to go to jail, that iced the cake of another crazy summer on the farm.

That farm season of apprentices had actually started out great. We already had one solid apprentice ready to come on board; in addition to digging the earth, he was very responsive to the idea of sharing in the morning meditation that Ricky now regularly engaged in. After a bunch of uninspiring interviews as we sought our second apprentice we received a call from Linus. His mother had heard me give a talk at a library a few towns over and had thrust our newsletter in front of him. Apparently, he needed to do community service hours: a lot, and soon. Our phone conversation carried on with ease; he seemed an intelligent and amicable guy.

"So, does the idea of working with the land for a couple of days interest you?" I asked.

"Actually, yes, my interests in cultivation are the reason I need to do community service."

It was as I'd surmised: community service after jail time done for cannabis cultivation elsewhere, and now he was back home to regroup.

We invited Linus to come volunteer a day on the farm. He worked hard and well, and the conversation was good. Ricky and I gave each other that 'this might work' look and, after a brief check-in with each other, asked him if he might want to apprentice for the season. He called the next day and said yes.

For the next few months, all went really well. He and our other apprentice Jon hit it off and were a great team and positive presence through spring and early summer. No red flags were raised when we heard his van return in the middle of an early July night. Things continued as usual for the next month or so. It wasn't until mid-August, during the heart of the harvest, and with everything about to hit high gear in preparation for our annual Garlic and Arts Festival, that Linus told us about his idiotic escapades.

From the start, we knew he'd done three months in a county jail in another state before coming to us, trading time for a felony and landing a misdemeanor instead. He was honest and seemed reflective. But, either he hadn't learned his lesson or class privilege clouded his judgment. He told us the story of what happened that July weekend he had off from the farm. Linus had gone up north where he had been living previously and picked up a few pot plants, making them his passengers right on the front floor of his truck. Stopping for gas at what would turn out to be a closed station, a cop drove by as Linus was pressing his face to the glass door to see if it really was closed. The police officer had run his plate number, found his record, and searched his van. Staring back at him were the barely concealed plants. Linus was released (which we believe must have come at the cost of providing a few names). He returned to the farm and said nothing until this moment when his court date was imminent, explaining why he was leaving within days to redon the orange smock rather than continue to enjoy the Town of Orange landscape.

We had planned a day and night getaway to Vermont to take a breath of family time and gather some energy for the rest of season, and decided to continue with the plan even after hearing Linus' news. Instead of a relaxing retreat, Ricky spent twenty-four hours in a motel room with the covers over his head, exhausted and depressed. Upon return home, we regrouped, and set out to find ourselves someone to fill in for the next six weeks. I put up a call on a message board while presenting at a local farming conference and Rochelle replied that very weekend. We were desperate. It was the harvest season and a month to the Garlic and Arts Festival. Jon was great but we needed another person. There was no time for relaxed tea and conversation, or the Shackleton test.

It ranged from okay to awful as she emerged as an erratic temperament, one day sweet and full of rage the next. We grinned and bared it over the month for which she had signed on, at this point just hoping to finish the season with our farm and marriage intact. When the agreed-upon departure date approached and we reminded her of such, she exploded, unfurling a range of expletives long-brewing in her shaky psyche. We knew this had little to do with the month she had spent with us, but she owned a big axe. I made sure our toddler was safe in the house and stood a few feet back as Ricky kindly but firmly thanked her as she packed her car and axe, and drove off.

Fortuitously, just days before Rochelle's departure, the repeat offense that would have undoubtedly kept a young man of color behind bars for many years was somehow turned around and Linus suddenly returned to our farm and life. Festival over, garlic sold, fall crops planted, and marriage unbruised, we finished out the season with our hardworking and amicable, albeit jail-brushing apprentice.

# The Worms' Perfect Singles Bar

When Deb and I purchased the long-abandoned farm in Orange with a plan to grow vegetables on the rocky land, it was what we could afford. On my previous farm we used roll after roll of black plastic to keep weeds down for the row crops. When I layered the first loads of cardboard on the edge of one field, our new neighbors looked on curiously, perhaps thinking we were hoarders gone off the deep end. To re-use this free resource made from trees seemed like the right thing to do. I had no idea then that this would turn into one of my great passions. It was to be the start of my long-term love affair with cardboard and the birth of 'The Cardboard Method,' my signature contribution to no-till ecological agriculture.

I had farmed larger acreage with tractors. While it was "organic," the pace and lifestyle was not sustainable. I wanted to farm in a way where nature led the way over machinery. My dad would often grumble, "Ricky, why don't you get a tractor?" Some friends would ask the same. I've never been the type that likes machinery or technology much. We all dance to a different drummer; since the age of fifteen I've followed my heart against the tide of societal and family expectations. Some may call me a Luddite and I'm okay with that. Having had machinery on my first farm, I know that when you have a tractor you are always thinking *I should use this thing because I bought it* and then try to use it in as many ways as possible rather than be creative to figure out how to grow food without. After our time spent in Iraq on the International Pilgrimage For Peace and Life and seeing the aftermath of the first Gulf War, I felt even more resolved to not contribute to the human cost of running equipment on fossil fuels. Through experimentation favoring nature over machinery, I worked to create a successful no-till farm that uses complementary techniques to eliminate fossil fuels and weeding, conserve water and labor, and let nature do more of the work. And, my relationship with the soil and plants has been enhanced in a way that is personally and deeply nourishing.

Worms, microbes, and fungi have become my best allies. I knew that tilling was not the way to enhance these populations. Worms are

Ricky shares his love of worm-till methods.

special, and part of why I continue to love farming after thirty years. They proved essential in transforming acidic, barren land into balanced, rich soil. I consider myself a worm farmer, not in the traditional sense of raising worms in bins and tanks, but throughout all of our growing beds. I like to think of my technique not as no-till, but as worm-till. They do incredible work and reproduce freely, adding nutrient rich castings as they go.

When word of our farm and no-till methods began to get out, people started to call with the hope to drop by to 'pick our brains' (our least favorite expression). These calls started to come in several times a week, and visits could take a couple of hours. You simply can't run a farm this way. At the same time, we wanted to inspire gardeners and farmers to ditch their rototiller and connect with the soil and to each other. So, in addition to workshops for farmers and college students, we began to offer free farm tours three times a year for the general public. This was much more manageable and sustainable for us.

We always begin a tour with a circle and welcome before leading the group down our farm road. Many pause at the words and images of

Thich Nhat Hanh, Nelson Mandela, Cesar Chavez, Angela Davis, and other activists painted on signs along the path through the woods, on the greenhouses, and among the patchwork of cardboard-covered fields that make our farm look a little different from most others.

As we gather the group in front of one of the fields, I suggest that any young ones in the crowd close their ears as I launch into my favorite spiel: "Cardboard is the perfect singles bar for worms. Worms want to be aboveground to have sex, but being above the soil makes them easy prey for birds. So cardboard laid on the ground makes the most perfect environment while protecting them. It's dark, it's moist, and promotes a free buffet." I share this with every group that visits our farm and education center and it usually gets their attention. "If you remember one thing from this tour," I stress, "cardboard is the perfect worm food and worm castings are the perfect plant food—it's a beautiful, symbiotic relationship."

My greatest joy is showing people all of the areas where cardboard has been placed over the years, and their look of amazement when they see the amount of worms and the layer of castings under the cardboard. They are blown away to see that in most of our growing beds the soil is now so rich and loose that I can insert my arm up to my elbow with ease. People often ask whether cardboard is safe. Corrugated cardboard made with soy inks and hide glue (high in protein which also attracts the worms) is safe and actually promotes soil life.

The Cardboard Method is the first of three techniques that comprise our no-till toolbox that has evolved over two decades—by necessity, and with many lessons from nature. Used for different and complementary reasons, these methods build organic matter, promote beneficial soil microbes and mycorrhizal fungi, reduce weeds, conserve water and labor, and respond to climate change by helping to keep carbon in the earth. With these techniques, I am now able to manage several acres of intensively planted crops largely on my own. We no longer have live-in apprentices and instead evolved to weekly volunteers, which works well. Deb's primary work shifted towards running our education programs and nonprofit wing once the farm infrastructure was established. These connected-yet-separate roles offered relationship balance

Cardboard mulch keeps weeds at bay, retains and controls moisture, and feeds the life in the soil, that then nourishes the plants. We call it a 'self-sustaining' method, as after a few years it is no longer necessary to add compost and other fertilizers; feeding the life in the soil with cardboard results in the fertility needed.

and sustainability to the whole. My ability to farm with less labor, increased efficiency, and personal equanimity became essential as well as enjoyable. Cardboard remains my favorite way to open up new land. It is my weed control, moisture control, and worm food that results in nutrient rich castings—my primary fertilizer. One full load of large sheets of cardboard gathered from furniture, bike, or appliance stores in my Ford F-350 will cover an area 35-by-100 feet that I then layer with mulch hay. I've used cardboard in many ways, at all times of the year. It softens quickly with some moisture, enabling me to use a simple dibbler hand tool to make holes right through it to plant seedlings, leaving the surrounding hay-covered cardboard as mulch. In the areas where I have been using cardboard for at least five years, the growing beds have become so established and rich that I have been able to cut out additional compost and other soil amendments upon seeing that the cardboard and subsequent worm and microbial activity is enough to feed the plants. Cardboard is a huge benefit that cuts the cost of acquiring compost or other fertilizers, as well as labor, time, and expense.

My second tool in the Seeds of Solidarity Farm no-till toolbox is what many growers in Europe call occultation—the use of darkness. When I shared this with a group of ten other farmers in a multi-day meeting with researchers from Cornell University, they all looked at me as if I was a little crazy. When I want bare ground to sow cover crops or scatter sow seed for salad greens such as in our hoop houses (and without having to remove the cardboard), I use silage tarps. Large silage tarps (also called bunker or panda covers) create darkness to rapidly turn plant biomass into mulch and leave bare soil below. Seedlings thrive in cardboard mulch, but to direct sow seeds like cover crops or salad greens, silage tarps are a great method. These are much thicker and more durable than regular black plastic, last many years, and can be easily moved around a farm or garden as needed. Weeds or cover crops below die and become mulch that is either transplanted into or raked off into paths and composted in place. Once the season is going, there are so many pieces of farming that demand attention. Silage tarps give me breathing room. Staying on top of weeds is one of the great stresses of farming. To be able to cover a field once crops have been harvested,

Silage tarps are used to return biomass to the soil and create bare ground for seed or cover crops.

wait until plant material breaks down, then decide how to best use an area eases my mind.

As my third no-till tool, I use a variety of cover crops to suppress weeds, invite pollinators, fix nitrogen, and serve as a green manure. These can be sowed individually or as a cocktail of annual or perennial plants, depending on the setting and need. Cover crops limit erosion, can loosen soil with their roots, and put carbon back where we want it: in the earth. While many believe they need to use machinery to incorporate cover crops, there are other ways. Cover crops can be crimped at the base of the stem with a rake (or for larger areas, with a roller) so that they become mulch that the soil life will decompose, aiding soil fertility. Silage tarps can be used to incorporate cover crops into the soil rather than tilling them in. Land that is covered with a silage tarp in early spring will warm up more quickly for planting, as well as activate the life in the soil to nourish the crops to come. While we do not raise livestock, cover crops are also essential in creating healthy, balanced pastures for grazing.

Diverse plantings of cover crops fix nitrogen, store carbon, and invite pollinators before being covered with cardboard or silage tarps to decompose and enrich the soil.

Our motto at Seeds of Solidarity is "Grow Food Everywhere." If we are to truly feed communities and ourselves we cannot depend solely on existing farmland but must create community-based gardens and small farms in as many settings as possible. Building soil and growing on land that is not considered agricultural is critical to our food supply. River bottomland—once highly sought after—now gets 100-year floods three years in a row! Chances of GMO drift are high when growing in an established farm community. The price of good farmland when you are competing with housing lots and

Our microbe digester for peecycling: urine can be safely transformed into a free, phosphorus rich fertilizer for seedlings and non-edible plant parts.

A lush greenhouse is paradise, and the harvested crops beam with vitality.

Home Depots is usually out of the question. In addition, urban land and lots are often places where soil with toxins needs to be microbe-cleansed and have its fertility developed; the practices I describe are applicable in these settings as well.

No-till practices that create and enhance a living soil rich with worms, microbes, and mycorrhizal fungi are key to a much-needed, sacred relationship with the soil that feeds us. Along the way I have come across quotes from other 'outside the box' thinkers that reaffirmed my commitment to farming without machinery. To remember the words of some great thinkers and elders, I post quotes on our farm buildings from teachers such as Masanobu Fukuoka: "When you work with machines you become like them: you become dead yourself." Another of our signs offers a Hopi saying: "The traditional farmer does not jump into his task with powerful machinery, he gradually blends with the field so everything will live in harmony."

We are not alone in our journey. Only about two percent of the world's farmers use fossil fuel-driven machinery; the rest rely on animal power and their own hands. Our methods are not new, but old in many ways. They resemble many indigenous methods and agroecological techniques used throughout the world by farmers who cultivate small patches of land intensively and replenish nutrients with local resources and traditional wisdom. I arrived at 'no-till farming for life' by coming to know and respect the soil in my hands. My hands are my primary tools along with a few handheld implements, my shovel, and my wheelbarrow. I'm doing what I love. I hear the birds while I work, not the constant hum of machinery. And I am not spending any of my days fixing equipment, as many farmers do.

Many struggle to figure out how to have a balanced life—the life they really want to live each day. Thirty plus years after my first market garden at the New Alchemy Institute, I still farm and I still love to grow food. What I grow and how I grow it continues to develop and change. As a farmer, what I see missing in most articles and conversations surrounding local agriculture is the spirit of the land, all that is not seen, and the sacredness that connects food to our universe. We need to bring spirit into the conversation. Food is our life force, our connection to the earth. As farmers, it is critical both to keep ourselves healthy for the long haul and to leave the land better than it was when we started working it. After farming for many decades now, the practices I've arrived at, continue to explore, and love to share nourish me as a human being. They also enhance the life in the soil, the life force of the food that I grow.

## *Surreal Times on the Farm*

Ah, those pictures of the smiling farmers gracing the pages of local food magazines, joyfully extending stunning baskets of glowing veggies! We look like that sometimes. But Ricky and I definitely did not look like that the day we got ripped off *and* Donald Trump was nominated for President. Nor did we look like that within this same 24-hour period when a huge tree almost fell on Ricky just as my ninety-plus year old in-laws were on their way over. Or during that same concentrated day of craziness when a woman called claiming her foster daughter was having sex with her boyfriend on our farm. And a few other things that make you look up and say, "Are you there, God? It's me, Deb."

Hit rewind. That particular surreal day actually started off quite sweetly. I woke up thinking of our high-school-aged son Levi in Yosemite Valley on a summer trip and his first solo transcontinental journey. He was without cell service once he landed in Fresno, but we could imagine him energized by a group of twenty-four other young people, packing and unpacking their backpacks and readying their bear canisters for a nine-day trek into one of the most stunning wilderness areas on earth.

Ricky was already up and out as I put the tea kettle on. He'd risen at 5:00 A.M. to water the greenhouses before starting Day Two of what was looking to be a stellar garlic harvest, even after sleepless nights of drought-filled days, wondering if our prime market crop would be a wash. This is the stuff that drive farmers over the edge, so I am thankful he meditates. I had just read a sweet morning note from him left on the counter and taken my first sip of strong tea when he came back in for breakfast. "We were ripped off last night," he said. Someone had mangled, then emptied the bolted cash box in our innocent self-serve farm stand. A wash of violation swept through my body with the sadness of all things sad that happened in the last two weeks: two more Black men shot by police; police killed by a man trained and traumatized by the military; a truck barreling through Nice on Bastille Day, killing families and further feeding Islamophobia among those who spend too many hours a day watching Fox News.

As Ricky was investigating the cash-box shelf damage, he saw the little plastic case in which I had created a good luck charm of beads and stones in the colors of Elegba, remover of obstacles, for Levi. Ricky traced it back to our old Subaru parked near the farm stand, where he found the glove box ajar and key stolen. When the police arrived, they confirmed what we had suspected: someone desperate for change had gone through the car, thought the good luck charm to be a pillbox, and continued on to the farm stand. All the while, the German Shepherd across the street had apparently ignored the light sensor and the commotion. He wasn't used to this happening in our trusting neighborhood and it hadn't happened in many years.

All of this took time and emotional precedence over an 11:00 a.m. photo shoot I'd all but forgotten, now twenty minutes away. My hair was a mess and held out of my face with a produce twist-tie. I had not yet showered to rinse away the coating of the previous night's hot-flash sweat now mixed with early morning heat and farm dust. I slipped into the shower then threw on jeans and a vintage Garlic and Arts Festival t-shirt. I took another sip of tea (now cold and bitter) and headed back up the farm road to meet the photographer. I cut a bundle of purple coneflowers on the way to brighten the photo as well as my sad heart.

Across from the garlic fields, farm apprentices and a few workers hired for the harvest had circled and were wiping soil from the bulbs as Ricky methodically and rapidly dug up one after the next, moving down the row on his calloused knees. Everyone was settled into farm 'chairs'—fifty-five gallon barrels cut in half that make great baskets when upright with ropes secured to each side, and good seats for a crowd when turned upside down. Quentin, a wonderful young man from Ecuador seeking farming experience while spending a month with some friends of ours, was seated next to Owen, our steadfast and cheerful high school apprentice. Friend and past intern Heather was there, as well as Toby and Julia, hardworking stoners who were bartering time on the farm in exchange for a little piece of our land on which they had built a modular tiny house that suited their transient (but moving towards rooted) lifestyle. Next in the circle was Ashleigh, a fifteen-year-old in DCF custody whose foster mom had reached out to see if she could fulfill her required community service hours with us. The crew was completed with a trio from a local agency that supports adults with developmental disabilities who came every Tuesday for a few hours.

Julia's brother Frankie had slept over at their place and had sped off early, supposedly to repair a chainsaw to help with the fallen tree that narrowly missed Ricky during the previous day's wind storm. He returned, pulled up a barrel-seat and joined in with the rest of the garlic cleaner/bundlers. As usual on days with a big crew, the conversation flowed as the garlic bundles accumulated. Meanwhile, a kind neighbor had shown up and made short work of the tree across the driveway with his functioning chainsaw.

The photographer from the local chamber of commerce came careening down the driveway, apparently oblivious to the fact that she had just passed by all the people and shots. I walked down the driveway for the eighth time that morning and retrieved her just as a few festival committee members arrived for the photo shoot. I now had forty minutes to greet the group and have the photos taken before I needed to leave to pick up my in-laws who had arrived the day before and were staying at a local bed and breakfast. Somehow, we managed a few photos of organizers displaying handmade objects with the garlic harvest in the background. Contrary to images that depict life on the farm as a bowl of cherries, sometimes life on the farm is just this way.

By early afternoon, the crew had moved to another field and was assembled under a canopy across from the house surrounded by garlic varieties with names like Armenian, Romanian Red, and Georgian Crystal to ready for hanging and curing. Ricky's parents Sue and JB were provided with lawn chairs of honor as the group conversation moved from topic to topic.

I headed inside to replenish water for the group, enjoying the relative normalcy of that simple moment. As the jug filled, I answered a call from Ashleigh's foster mother. Early that day in the garlic bundling circle, conversation had turned from political to personal as Sue and JB asked the young people a bit about their lives. Ashleigh took the opportunity to share a few tidbits from her childhood of neglect and stream of foster homes. It was unusual to have someone this young volunteer on a regular farm day; we reserved another day of the week for our SOL Garden program for teenagers, which united a diverse group of local youth in a six-month experience. But SOL Garden was well underway for the season and Ashleigh just needed a short-term community service stint. She had only come to the farm a few times, and had not really taken to the soil or the work. We had come to love spending time with local teens in SOL Garden who found healing and community on the land, but this connection with her was just not clicking. From where I stood filling the water jug, I could see the circle across the way as I answered the phone in the kitchen. Ashleigh had, as usual, positioned herself near Owen, having revealed her crush over the few Tuesdays she had been coming to the farm. We had done our best to keep them working separately as he was clearly not interested and uncomfortable, and her persistence distracted his excellent and focused work. Her foster mother offered an awkward pleasantry before asking about the level of supervision on the farm.

"What's the actual question?" I asked.

"Ashleigh told her foster sister that she's having sex with her boyfriend while she's at your farm."

I spit the water I was drinking into the sink and took a breath filled with hope that this day would soon end. I told her this was definitely not happening, and that it was important to us that she call Ashleigh's case worker immediately to get my response on record. I told her I'd talk to Ricky to see how to proceed. I felt bad for this foster mother, just trying to do her best. And I felt bad for Ashleigh—but we hardly knew her, and couldn't keep her coming to the farm out of kindness and some belief we could help her. We'd been down that road before with other kids. And we definitely could not do it at the expense of our reputation. And we certainly didn't need DCF showing up with a deluge of paperwork. It crossed my mind for a moment that Ashleigh had brought some loser guy over the night before and that maybe they'd been the ones in our cash box. This is what can happen when you get ripped off! It sucks to start thinking and looking at people that way. But what I didn't know then was that the person who'd stolen our cashbox was closer than we thought.

The surreal day finally ended. Somehow, through it all, the rafters in the drying area filled with really good-looking garlic. The second day of the harvest was done, with seven more to go. Physically and emotionally exhausted, we capped the day with a pleasant-enough dinner out with Ricky's parents. I sipped my second glass of red wine and felt my shoulders start to settle back into place.

When Ashleigh arrived a week later for what would be her last day, we paired her with Diane, our most mature and trusted volunteer. I made everyone our usual Tuesday farm lunch of fresh salad and burritos. I timed my day to walk her up afterwards so I could be there when her foster mother's van arrived. I presented Ashleigh with a hastily assembled goodbye gift: a cookbook in a reusable shopping bag with a puppy on it, as I knew she loved animals. I directed my words to her and her foster mother simultaneously, "You've been a great worker, Ashleigh." The truth is not always best. Ashleigh and I hugged before she climbed in the back and immediately engaged with whatever video game her foster sibling had going. Her foster mom looked at me with some combination of knowing and regret. I tuned out as the foster mother's friend tried to extract advice about her wilting cucumber plants. I needed to go have a cup of tea alone. I needed to believe that it would rain and relieve my husband and so many other farmers of the weeks of waiting. I just needed a little break.

I walked back down the path to our farm. Remnants of the ten days of garlic harvest—now close to over—were strewn in the cleaning area: coffee cups and benches, bits of twine, and a t-shirt indistinguishable from a rag. There were colorful marking tapes labeled with the names of the sixteen varieties that had been planted clove by clove the year before, totaling over a linear mile of garlic. I picked up an overturned vase that still held the now-wilted purple coneflowers left in haste after the photo shoot a week earlier.

About six weeks later, one of our suspicions about who might have robbed our farm stand was confirmed. Turns out, Julia's brother Frankie had handed a teller a note and robbed a nearby bank without a gun or facemask. Then he robbed another in New Hampshire before heading south for Charlotte, North Carolina, where he was matched with wanted images. But the police had not yet caught up to him when they pulled onto Chestnut Hill Road, just as Ricky was making one of many Garlic and Arts Festival runs with our truck piled high with tables, crates, and banners to set up for the event now just days away. He'd put his hand out of the truck window with a friendly wave in passing, but passing was not what they had in mind when they blocked the narrow dirt road. Their car doors opened simultaneously and six state troopers in SWAT team gear got out to question Ricky. This was the scene I came upon while casually strolling up to get the mail. Frankie's ex-girlfriend had told the police he had a sister who worked on a farm out our way, which was unfortunately and indeed us. They searched Julia and Toby's tiny house and came up empty, for which I was both relieved and sorry, wanting him caught by now so this could all just end.

After the cops left, I thought back to that garlic harvest day when I saw Frankie behind the screen door the morning right after the theft when I'd come to tell Toby and Julia what had happened. I'd heard a little voice inside me go *Could it be Frankie?* Looking back and retracing the moments, I remembered he'd taken off quickly to get that chainsaw, even when I'd told Toby we were all set, and thought Frankie had heard me. But when he'd returned and joined the circle with us, cleaning garlic while sharing his hopes to go to auto body school and his sadness about his separation from his girlfriend and their two little kids, I'd felt badly for thinking he could have been the culprit. This, in fact, is how someone addicted to opiates can roll. But we didn't know it then, nor did Toby and Julia, who thought he'd been substance-free for a while. Frankie was placed into custody, and hopefully received the treatment he needed along with jail time.

Ricky hadn't wanted to tell me that after the big rip-off someone else continued to try to get into the box that he now made sure he emptied each day. He hadn't wanted to worry me. The pieces now all fit together, shadowed by great sadness for another life impacted by drug addiction.

We heard Ashleigh might have moved on to another foster home. Quentin returned to Ecuador and Owen to finish high school, their presence captured in photos of them smiling amidst big barrels of garlic. The garlic sold well at that year's festival, with some reserved and planted later amid the fall splendor, with the stories of an unforgettable garlic harvest in the cloves. The crew of farm volunteers dwindled with the season and so, too, the conversations quieted. The chilly days began to replace the memory of the drought and dust of that summer. The next time we had a farm photo taken of us holding a glowing bowl of veggies, we actually looked—and were—pretty happy.

*Excerpts from the Cooler Blog:*
*Notes to Customers on the Farm Stand Fridge*

*June 8*
The greens are medicine, growing in a balanced soil, never tilled. The model of small stores and farm stands throughout every community is the future. In order to bring economic sanity back we must purchase from our neighbors—then we will really know where our hard-earned money is going. Let us all work to keep money in our own communities so it can support all our life-affirming visions vs. all we see on the news.

Be well and may you walk in peace,

Ricky

*June 28*
Localizing our economy and community! For years I went off-farm to deliver produce. It was enjoyable at first but the last few years, no fun. May we all find ways to make 'our living' close to home.

P.S. The tomatoes and eggplants are really coming along.

Ricky

*July 18*

We are back from speaking on Monhegan Island in Maine. In the late 1800s that small island grew eighty acres of food—today very little is grown but the movement is happening. If you are not already powering your home off a renewable energy source—solar, wind, hot water—get going, start planning. Islands are feeling the pressures of what is happening all across the planet—be prepared! No other creature would live so far away from their food source as we do.

Good luck and enjoy the process,

Ricky

*August 29*

We survived the hurricane of 2011. Many farms did not fare well. When I was looking for my first farm twenty-five years ago the place to look for was river bottomland. Now river bottomland gets 100-year floods three years in a row! Things have changed and we must adapt. Farming up in the hills, cities, suburbs—making soil is the future. May all neighborhoods everywhere come together to create resilient and healthy communities.

In solidarity,

Ricky

*September 18*

Life without petroleum is coming to a neighborhood near you. We must prepare in a loving way, not from fear. This is a good thing as the so-called first world lifestyle is killing the rest of the planet. May this neighborhood be an example of food resilience in the post-petroleum era.

Enjoy the peppers,

Ricky

*October 11*

If we asked people *Would a garlic and arts festival work in Orange?* years ago, most folks would have said no. If we asked could we sell lots of produce out of a self-serve stand way out here, what would people have said? The message is follow your hearts and dreams!

Thank you all,

Ricky

*Field Guide for Chapter Two*
*Grow Food Everywhere: Farming for Life*

## Questions to Ponder: Food and Spirit

- If you don't currently grow any of your own food, what are some barriers? Are you afraid of doing it wrong? Do you have access to land? Is your physical mobility limited? Do you have enough time?

- If you do grow your own food, what techniques or values are important to you? What is your next goal or challenge (fruit, animals, medical herbs, rooftops, providing food to others)?

- What resources are available to grow food for yourself or community (land/space, healthy soil/compost, tools, mentors/support, water)? How can you increase access to these for yourself and others?

- How do or can you integrate your spiritual life with the practice of growing food?

## Down to Earth: *Do It Yourself*

### *No-Till Gardening for Life with the Cardboard Method*

To build local food self-reliance, we need accessible, affordable, and fun practices that mimic nature, decentralize food production, and engage more people in cultivating the earth in order to Grow Food Everywhere. At Seeds of Solidarity, we place cardboard on land to foster worms, microbes and mycorrhizal fungi that decompose the cardboard and build a fertile soil ecosystem. In addition to an increase in worm reproduction and fertile castings (worm poop), using cardboard as mulch helps balance moisture, keep weeds down, and create no-till carbon sinks that retain rather than release $CO_2$ into the atmosphere. Cardboard—a waste product available in most communities—is key to growing gardens on lawns, schoolyards, and municipal lots for opening up and improving plots of land.

### *How to Create a Self-Sustaining Cardboard-Method Garden*

Worms and microbes decompose cardboard year-round, leaving well-aerated soil rich in worm castings in its place. If you put cardboard on a new area or existing garden at the end of the season in the fall, it will be largely decomposed by the spring—easy to dibble through or dig holes in for seedlings. You can also lay cardboard down in early or mid-spring for planting that same season. We recommend the following approach for planting seedlings (also called "transplants" or "starts," these are small vegetable plants already started that you have grown yourself or purchased from a local farmer).

1) Lay down large pieces of cardboard (sheets or well-flattened boxes) to create whatever size garden you wish or your space can accommodate. You do not need to cut or pull any weeds or grass—just cover it! Be sure there is at least a three-inch overlap between pieces of cardboard so there are no gaps. Cover cardboard with mulch hay or well-rotted leaves. If a windy day or season, water the cardboard well to make it heavy and stable or add a few large rocks or logs to hold it down.

2) When it is an appropriate time in the season to plant your seedlings (refer to information that tells you when it is safe to plant cool- and/

or warm-weather-loving crops) use a box cutter to cut holes in the cardboard spaced appropriately for whatever you are planting (e.g. kale can be 15" apart while tomatoes 3' apart). Make each hole about 6" to 1' in diameter—again, depending on plant size. A clothesline strung between pieces of rebar pounded into the ground can help you make holes in a nice line.

3) Shovel out the existing soil in each hole and replace with (or mix with) rich, fully decomposed compost (we like chicken compost).

4) Put a transplant in each hole and water it in well. You can always plant part of your garden with cool-weather crops (kale, broccoli, chard) in late spring, then make holes for and add hot-weather crops in early June.

Voilà! The cardboard around the plants will keep weeds down and moisture in, all while feeding the worms and microbes to help make the whole area richer for next year.

Another beauty of the no-till method is the simple tools: a box cutter, dibble, and a hori-hori or sturdy soil knife are all you need.

Yes, you can continue to lay down cardboard (see step one) at any time of the year to expand your garden area or keep bare ground covered until you are ready to plant again.

## Awaken The Power: *Contemplative Practice*

### *Create a Land Mandala*

Making a mandala from gathered or found symbolic items is a beautiful way to connect to a familiar or new place, honor a changing season, or open an event by establishing sacred space. The mandala is a powerful symbol representing a microcosm of the universe. Translated from the Sanskrit for "circle," the mandala is often found in Hindu and Buddhist traditions. The creation of and contemplation on the mandala is a form of meditation.

This unifying activity can be done alone, as a couple, as a family, or with a group of any size. It is possible in garden, field, forest, or city lot. The creation of a mandala is a beautiful ritual to open the spring season, waking up with the land and honoring the earth before planting; it is also fitting at the close of the season to celebrate the harvest with its bounty incorporated into the mandala (to then be eaten or shared). While those present might bring something to add to a mandala if they are prepared in advance, it is also powerful to simply open your eyes and gather what you find in the moment.

While sitting or standing in a circle, start with a short, silent meditation with a focus on gratitude for the many gifts of the land. Take anywhere from a couple to ten minutes depending on the length of time you have and the comfort of the space for standing or sitting.

Maintaining the quiet, invite everyone present to take a short walk in silence to gather some natural or found objects that speak to them. Additionally, people can bring things with them that they will add to the mandala so long as they are from or will return to nature. The spontaneity of incorporating that which is found strengthens the realization that this type of everyday ritual can be done anywhere. With a large group, everyone needs to gather but one thing. If there are only a few people, you can bring an assortment of items in advance for people to choose from. If a group is to be together over time, add to your mandala over the course of a few days. We often start a workshop with a mandala, adding emergent prose, art, and ideas around the circle over the workshop's duration.

At the sound of a bell, all return to the chosen, central spot. Invite someone to start (perhaps the eldest and youngest participants) by placing something at the center. Others then place their items in turn as they are moved. A mandala is most often symmetrical and so participants can add their findings with this concept in mind—but no need to be rigid. It is nice to form the mandala in silence.

When all items have been laid down, people may choose to share something about what they offered and what it means to them, or they may remain quiet and just listen. Sometimes people find more things right at their feet to add, and that is fine.

Leave the mandala in place as a gift to the land. Close with a relevant reading, song, or ululation!

### Ten Ways to Grow and Enjoy Food for Health

- Buy only GMO-free seeds and seedlings from companies you can trust.
- Grow what you enjoy eating!
- Seek a few simple tools you love.
- Build soil using local resources (cardboard, compost, wood chips, seaweed, leaf mulch, and pee-cycling).
- Make compost and/or keep a worm bin.
- Work with the seasons—use easily constructed 'low tunnels' of hoops and greenhouse plastic to grow three seasons in cooler climates.
- Practice and promote container gardening with growing bags and other containers (great for urban areas and temporary housing).
- Learn to gather and enjoy edible plants, mushrooms, and herbs from the wild.
- Dry, preserve, ferment, and can food; grow food that is good medicine, too!
- Grow things that store well during the winter (squash, potatoes, herbs).

# Chapter Three

# The Sacred Sacrifice:
# Living with Less is More

## Build a House, Keep that Spouse

"Maybe you should drink a cup of coffee."

"I quit drinking coffee," I replied to Ricky while nursing our week-old baby, perched on the edge of the bed that took up a large portion of the room that was our entire home.

Many months earlier, I had applied for a yearlong fellowship through the Corporation for National Service. It seemed ideal. If I received it, I could design and execute a research project while working full time from home and receive a $25,000 stipend for the year. I'd only have to make three trips to Washington, D.C. and, well, figure out how to actually work full-time from a one-room home with a newborn and simultaneously help build our house. Um, and run all the new programs of our organization. Right—and launch the first ever North Quabbin Garlic and Arts Festival.

The morning after I gave birth, I got the call that I'd made it to the finalist round. Ricky told me the news as I awoke in the Franklin Medical birthing center with a healthy, little pink human snuggled at my side. I was not exactly fully rested after a sixty-hour labor in 100 plus degree heat following a noble effort at a homebirth. The fellowship agency wanted to schedule a phone interview with six honchos at the D.C. office in the coming week. Thank God it was not in-person—I hadn't told them I was pregnant. I know they couldn't discriminate against me, but I'd never done this before—attempted to be a professional with a brain full of smart ideas and a mother with a brain full of hormones at the same time. So I simply hadn't told them. And I sure wasn't planning on breaking the news during my interview, either.

Ricky offered me coffee the morning of the interview before realizing we didn't have any. My vagina was still torn apart, swollen boobs made me scream at the slightest touch, hormones made me cry at the slightest glimmer of worldly beauty, and now there was no option in sight for recovering from being awake for three days while the little baby I was now totally in love with sent waves of killer contractions to open the gate for his arrival. So I heated up a kettle with the water we hand-pumped from our well and made a very strong cup of black tea. And did the interview. And got the fellowship.

A month later, as the date approached for the first trip to D.C. to meet with the other eleven practitioners chosen from across the country, I still hadn't told the project director that I had a newborn. I practiced: "I am *so* looking forward to meeting you and the other fellows! Oh! And my husband will be coming to D.C. along with our newborn— at our own expense of course. Just out of curiosity, will we be meeting at the same hotel as where we are staying?"

This was not mere curiosity. This was an urgent need to know how much milk I was going to have to pump before dawn if I was going to have to travel across the city without the hubby and the babe. It was a great relief to hear the male project director reply with enthusiasm and support. The first family flight was an adventure in packing with approximately six items of luggage for a fourteen-pound small person. It was good that I'd practiced pumping, as a minor hurricane hit D.C. while we were there, separating milk mom from husband and baby for a full day. Somehow, we made it.

Back home, we returned to balancing house-building, parenting a newborn, and living on a modest check from the fellowship that was our sole source of income for a year. We strived to stay loving through it all.

Our routine went something like this: each morning I'd get out of bed—we'd moved the futon mattress down from the tiny loft in the one-room cottage that we built pre-pregnancy (begun the day after we signed on the land, which happened to be the middle of winter). We had been so excited to break ground that we'd spent weeks carrying every stick of lumber 700 feet down a path from the main road to a clearing in the forest. It was—and still is—a sweet little place, but with no running water and only enough electricity to power a couple of lights and recharge a computer battery. After nursing the baby, taking a sponge bath, and having a bite to eat, I'd close the door to a closet-sized space that housed my computer, and worked all morning.

Meanwhile, Ricky would do his push-up ritual next to baby Levi (napping, if Ricky was lucky). Then they would read or play, do a diaper change or two, take a walk—truthfully I don't know exactly what they did. I knew if I paid any attention I wouldn't be able to cram a full day of work into four concentrated hours. If I didn't, the fellowship and Ricky's ability to pass the baby back to me at lunchtime would be kaput. Did I mention our cottage also housed one very large dog, one medium dog, and a cat?

After a little lunch, I'd shut off the trusty, clunky old computer and put down the phone. It was a Princess style with a flimsy cord woven through the trees outside to a temporary phone interface. I would close the door to the closet-turned-office and receive a most beautiful, squirming baby into my arms. Then Ricky would suit up into his insulated overalls, strap on his tool belt, and head up to the concrete slab and piles of lumber that would become our main house. He'd bang nails for as many hours as he could until dark. I nursed, made dinner, snuck in a few more calls related to my fellowship, did a little stretching while the baby napped, bundled the baby, brought Ricky tea or words of support, and tried not to go crazy.

Some days we got to work on building the house together, especially once the fellowship ended (successfully, with a published curriculum called *Schools Serving for Social Change*). I continued teaching and consulting to bring in money while we worked to grow the non-profit organization, build farmable soil on barren land, and continue to build the house. Once he was bipedal, Levi went off to a family childcare a few mornings a week. He also started helping with (or was at least very entertained by) the building— his expertise was being covered in sheetrock mud. The summer that Levi turned two, and after a long, trying winter with no shortage of cabin fever, we moved into the main

The little house the first winter, before stuccoing. Our first solar electric system powered a light and small fridge. Heavy snows added romance along with cabin fever by the second winter.

house and brought our first farm apprentices on to take our place in the beloved cottage. While it took several more years to finish the house, the first night in our own bedroom brought a sense of freedom and great gratitude. With Levi now in his own room, the opportunity for some long-overdue privacy and intimacy returned.

Fortunately, Ricky soon had a steady helper to get the main house finished.

When people come to visit now and see all we've built—a cottage, home, studio with guest loft, farm outbuildings, five greenhouses, and a farm stand—we try to paint a picture for them of how it began. It is not so much to marvel at the accomplishments as to express that creating the infrastructure took fifteen years of some crazy times. In case they were wondering, we mention there was no trust fund. What we had were winter days of little light, no running water, and countless walks down our long, icy driveway with a bundled baby strapped on back, groceries precariously balanced in a chipped plastic sled. There was a romance to it. There was stress. There was devotion. There was anticipation. There was nothing else we felt we should or wanted to be doing.

Years later, we've learned to schedule weekly meetings together to discuss all the pieces of our lives: parenting, the farm, programs and vision for our organization, scheduled presentations and teaching, social happenings, and the creation of this book. I don't remember having planned meetings in the early days, though. It was, in many ways, a more complicated time. It was, in many ways, a simpler time—intense but with fewer pieces before we had a full-fledged farm, active non-profit, and multifaceted festival to hold together. We developed ways of being efficient and supporting each other in our unique roles towards a common goal, a practice that we have since had many years to build on. We took a lot of walks filled with ideas and got to know our neighbors. We got to know each other, our relationship, our child, and ourselves more deeply. It was really hard and very beautiful. I can't imagine it any other way.

## Living and Crafting the Good Life

Thousands of people have visited Seeds of Solidarity since we first swung the scythe on an overgrown field and pounded the first of many nails. Many arrive with intrigue and questions as they seek examples of folks living outside of the box. On one of our Solidarity Saturday visiting days, an elementary school friend of mine named Dan came to visit with his family. We both grew up in the New York suburbs in an era of avocado-green kitchen cabinets and paneled station wagons. With tears in his eyes, Danny asked, "How did you do it? How did you break from the status quo?" This man, who I once shared a baby stroller with, looked at me inquisitively. He was essentially asking me what Deb and I ask ourselves: "How do you get out of the rat race with your heart intact in order to create the life you envision?"

We never got to meet them, but Helen and Scott Nearing and their pivotal book *Living the Good Life* served as inspiration for Deb and me when we were in our twenties and just starting out. The dwellings they created by hand were inspiring and infused with their philosophy of meaningful, hard work to achieve a beautiful life. At that time, there were not many models of couples forging and sharing their stories of an off-the-grid life, let alone couples perceived as strong equals. Scott's politics and Helen's spiritual journey were integral to their lifestyle and well-conveyed through their books and teachings. The 'can-do' way of life the Nearings exemplified was compelling, especially since Deb and I appeared to be headed that way too.

This 'just do it' attitude that Deb and I share is different than 'just wing it,' as we have worked diligently to gather many skills along the way to help make our dreams possible. When the spirit moves us we go into action. We have yet to write a business plan, but this doesn't mean that we don't plan. If we had carried out needs assessments to determine whether we could create a viable farm on barren land, start and fund a successful youth program, or attract people to a garlic and arts festival on a field in the middle of Orange, we would have likely been advised to stop before we even started. Yet all these have been successful—not without any shortage of effort and endurance, but with faith and fortitude proving more than financial figures.

Crafting a simple, energy-efficient, and comforting home was a plan that has been central to our ability to have an inspired space from which to grow a farm and non-profit. We have experienced and built community. We have raised a family.

My carpentry career began while I was farming in New York State in the late '80s. I needed money in the off-season to live and to re-invest in our farm each spring. The first crew I was on was quintessential redneck; I was the donut boy, getting coffee for the crew, picking up supplies, and cleaning the job site. I did learn some building amidst the abuse I received as the lowest man on the totem pole. It was enough to build myself a simple apartment in the barn on my New York farm, which was a great learning experience. My buddy Tim, who was working on another farm and also a budding builder, moved in with me. We had some incredible parties in the barn, and each evening after farming or building we'd run together in preparation for a half marathon. By then I had found a crew of talented hippie builders to join. They showed up at work parties as I began constructing a pole barn house on the farm. I never got to finish the structure as my farming partnership with Stuart came to an ugly close.

Down in Florida, I gained finish work experience rebuilding a heavily damaged historic home that once belonged to a sea captain and was now owned by a mutual friend. Three other friends and I brought the house back to its former glory in a hurricane-hit neighborhood. Post-hurricane Homestead was lawless like the Wild West. We worked

Our foundation choice was a frost-protected slab to save on costs and concrete. It would succeed in helping keep our house warm by absorbing winter sun through south-facing windows and naturally cool in the summer.

by day and at night I slept in a trailer in the driveway, often awakened by sounds of nearby gunfire. While I was in Homestead, my connection with Deb began to rekindle until we reconnected and got back together, this time for good. I worked one more winter in Homestead while Deb worked on her doctoral thesis. I trusted we would be together for life,

Our neighbors were and are such a blessing.

and now had the confidence and skills to build us a home someday.

Back together with Deb in Massachusetts, I worked with other builders on a few houses, putting as much aside as I could for our own land purchase. We got married. Then we went on the Pilgrimage. On the rare rest days, we began envisioning the home we would build on land we would seek upon return. The architecture and interiors we saw in Turkey (Deb's grandparents had emigrated from Turkey) had a big impact on our design aesthetics. We loved the colorful plaster arched doorways, hand-woven kilim rugs on walls, and cozy built-in seating areas in living spaces.

After finding land upon our return, and while building the 12-by-24-foot structure that we would live in for three years, we continued researching methods and materials as we tried to save enough money to at least start in on the main house. We spent time envisioning and sketching the spaces we wanted in our home. We liked the idea of an open floor plan for the downstairs. It would be cheaper and faster to create a fairly standard rectangular shape with a focus on extreme energy efficiency in our approach to construction, and save most of the creativity for textures and finishing details.

With a roll of drafting paper and a drawing board made of scrap plywood, Deb used her architectural drawing class experience and a how-to book to draft a set of plans for our main home that included all of the construction details and elevations. Given that our goal was to get a building permit, they didn't need to be architecturally pretty, just correct and sound. This saved us many thousands of dollars. We initially considered a straw bale home—but having helped build one before, I questioned their longevity in the Northeast and was nervous to invest every penny we had and years of time into a method that was still being perfected for our climate. We were most attracted to the shapes that could be sculpted into the walls given the thickness of the bales, as well as the plaster and stucco finishes. We realized we could do the same with a double wall construction approach, using blown-in cellulose to insulate nine-inch-thick walls. This insulation was not only well-tested in the building industry but was also a local material, produced nearby from the waste of regional paper mills. The permanence and quality of concrete also appealed to us. We researched building techniques for frost-protected slab (also known as an Alaskan slab or floating slab) as our foundation. We didn't want a basement—often home to mold and critters—so a slab felt right. It helped that we would save on the costs of excavation and concrete. Though many go with radiant floor heat in slabs, we decided against it. The use of radiant heat with solar was not yet fully developed, and the expense would have slowed our ability to frame and close in the house. Our builder friend Sully shared a great suggestion, which was to design for an attic with a higher knee-wall to allow for more space for storage or future finished space if desired. Before framing the building we spent many hours picking through windows stored in trailers at a salvage company. Although new and packaged, the flexibility to frame for the windows rather than buy pre-determined sizes also saved us many thousands of dollars.

As remains important in all we do, the relationships we developed through the home-building process mattered to us. We have a fond memory of sipping tea with the owner of the cellulose company, Tony Walker. Tony was a Buddhist practitioner who suggested some important construction details before we started framing that would make our super-insulated house even more efficient. We also contracted with a plumber who we knew, who was willing to have us help lay pipes for the rough plumbing in the slab, saving the cost of many hours of their labor. Friends Apollo and Sully joined us to pour the slab into a form Deb and I had prepared with layers of sand, gravel and insulation. The cured slab then served as the level surface on which I could frame the walls in preparation for wallraisings with neighbors.

A licensed electrician friend let me assist him with the labor of running all of the wiring that he then installed. The layout was quite similar to 'non-solar' new construction but with the addition of DC wiring for our refrigerator and a few other backup DC outlets which we might come to need. It all connected to an array of photovoltaic panels, related fuse-boxes, inverter, and charge controller. As with any building project, there were many conversations, adventures, and stories made.

Although I worked alone most of the time, our friend Bo arrived one day with perfect timing to help me get the final pieces of metal on the steeply pitched roof thanks to a climbing rope in his truck. We attached it to the bumper of our truck at one end, and over the peak and to my waist at the other as I screwed the last sheets in place. Once Deb and I had gotten the last of the blue board and sheetrock up, my friends Tim, Jolene, and Tony drove out from Ithaca. They spent several days helping us mix and spread plaster on the interior walls in shades of beige, gold, and deep red. While we did the lion's share of work to build our home, friends along the way not only brightened the experience, but also helped at critical times.

There has always been at least one dog in our lives, and Jackson and Chico were trusty sidekicks to our homebuilding. Jackson, the epitome of a mellow golden lab, connected my life in Ithaca to Homestead to Montague and then to Orange. Chico was a bizarre-looking brindle mutt who needed a good home. We even named our account at the local lumberyard after these two—Chico Jackson Builders. While most of the time they enjoyed wandering the woods at the edge of the home-site, our construction album includes a photo of Jackson and Chico curled up on an old futon as the cellulose sprayed down and around them like a blanket of warm snow.

There is a particularly memorable Jackson story that took place when the main house was but a foundation. It was autumn, and right around Deb's brother's birthday. He was passing through en route back to Boston, and we wanted to serve him dinner in our home-in-progress. While out buying building supplies, we picked up a special cake. We unloaded the day's cargo from the old silver pickup: light fixtures, concrete, a box of nails, and a box containing a lavishly layered chocolate cake. Deb asked where I'd put the cake, and as we simultaneously looked towards the construction site, all that was visible was the cake box, lid up, with giant lab snout fully immersed. They say chocolate can kill a dog, but not Jackson! A dog nap and a couple of burps—and a quick marital tiff over the lost cake—was followed by a nice dinner, a lot of laughter, and an apple pie, hastily located to replace its dessert predecessor.

Throughout the couple of years it took until we could move from the cottage into the main house, our lives continued with outside work, raising an infant, and starting our first educational program, SOL (Seeds of Leadership) Garden for local teens. As with any owner-built home, it took a while to do the finish work (which is still not completely finished). But the gift of time also allowed for ideas to evolve, free and upcycled materials to be found, and artful additions made to the original design and form.

Our greenhouses, buildings, and gardens evolved together and slowly expanded as money and time allowed.

The house reflects the handcrafted, artistic, and land-connected values that are important to us. A wood stove keeps us cozy all winter with just a cord and a half of wood from the local forest, and no additional fossil fuel-based heat.

Building is not only one of my passions, but an important skill for any farmer—be it using a level, doing the diagonals to square a greenhouse, or constructing tool sheds or other outbuildings. Such structures came to dot our homestead landscape over the years. As I built with love and local materials, my skills improved and concepts grew. From the early days of donut boy and hippie builder, I grew into a mason and fine woodworker driven by both economic necessity and a desire to live and craft a good life.

## *Of Life When Lightning Strikes*

I did not know what the small red light on the solar electric system panel meant, but I knew enough to know it was probably not supposed to be flashing. It had definitely not been on before the storm and nearby lightning strike the day before. I called Ricky in to take a look at the multi-component system in our mudroom that served our entire home and farm's electrical needs. We both just looked, as that was all we knew how to do at that point.

At that time there was not anyone in the local phonebook who was versed or specialized in solar, let alone solar companies calling left and right with various deals. To implement and install the modest photovoltaic system that would be the sole source of electricity for our home and farm, we had done a lot of reading and research. We visited several off-the-grid homes, then compiled a system with components—panels, inverter, batteries, and charge controller—from companies that we felt good about and whose products we could afford. Our wedding registry was even with Backwoods Solar an early solar supply company in Idaho. When our house construction project had exterior walls and a roof and before the insulation was blown in, we contracted with a friend who was a licensed electrician to run the wires in the house with Ricky and hook it up so all would be to code. The electrician had not done one before, because very few people had.

Our modest 1.5 kW solar electric system served us well from the day we were able to move into the house. Each day we learned a little more about the system and its capacity while enjoying the awareness of whether or not each sunrise was a good solar charging day. There was a magnificence to powering our lives with pure sunlight.

The red error light on the inverter (the brains of the system that turns DC to AC) was not about the sun, the wiring, or the quality of the system components. It was because lightning had struck very nearby the night before, and even the careful wiring and grounding could not fully mitigate its impact. Things happen in human and mechanical systems of every sort! When things occur in systems that are not an integral part of your self-sufficient energy lifestyle it is easy to assume that someone else is taking care of it, whatever the "it" is. In this case, we had to figure out what the "it" was ourselves. Neither of us was wired this way or found excitement in such pursuits. We pulled out the Trace Inverter handbook and started flipping through the many pages under Troubleshooting, following the steps to determine the meaning of the red error light. We clicked the cursor under the inverter menu category as directed by the handbook until it landed on what we were calling 'the boo-boo.' Once armed with some words from the error message indicator that included things like 'voltage' and 'regulator' rather than 'boo-boo,' I called Trace Inverters.

"You need to turn it all off now," said the not unkindly voice on the other end of the line.

This is generally not what you want to hear when you are hoping for something more like "It's nothing, just flip that little switch to the left and the red light will be gone." No such luck. The diagnostician on the phone explained the problem as a fried circuit that controlled the level of appropriate AC current going into the house. While a solar electric system is in fact generally much safer than the grid as it provides a more consistent, true sine wave current, something had gone amok with that bolt of lightning. So, we flipped the levers on the fuse boxes to shut the inverter down. Shutting the inverter down meant no electricity. And no electricity meant we could not pump water out of the well. And it was August—a very dry one. No water pump, dry crops...maybe dead crops. The fields were full with our harvest for market and for our livelihood. We could easily live without lights for a while and manage without refrigeration and showers. But without water for the crops? Not so much.

"It needs to go to a Trace Inverter technician," offered the diagnostician on the other side of the country. "And the nearest one is in Point Pleasant, New Jersey."

"Wow, they are going to come up here?" I exclaimed innocently and hopefully.

"No... you need to disconnect the system, unmount the inverter, and bring it to them."

We paused to contemplate this new level of understanding of our self-sufficient lifestyle. As mentioned, this was well before there was a plethora of solar electric companies ready to do your installation and explain your multiple choices and subsidy options, and well before renewable energy training programs or electricians existed who actually smiled rather than grimaced at your mention of a solar electric system. A trip to Point Pleasant was not in our immediate plans, even with the potential benefit of getting another tattoo while hanging out with a lot of New Jersey folks packed like plump, greasy sardines on the beach. (I got my first tattoo on the Jersey Shore way back when, before there were as many tattoo artists as there are solar companies now). We flipped the inverter off and called the nearest qualified Trace inverter repairman in Point Pleasant.

"The only other option," said the second, kind and helpful but geographically distant person of the day, "is if you can find someone who is really skilled at fine circuitry work. I could FedEx you the part and they could give it a try, but I'd be surprised if they could do it."

Well, we were surprised that we had made it as far as we had in our lives lived outside the box, so what the heck, why give up now. Plus, the universe can be super-helpful in situations like this. Up our farm road and across the street lived our neighbor Stefan, an organ builder who we were just getting to know. We knew he worked with circuit boards in the masterpieces he repaired and built. We knew he was German and Germanic in his precise ways. And we were aware of our innate hesitancy inherited by many Jews of our generation: fear of all things German. Our neighbor relations had been amicable so far. Ricky went up to his house, explained our predicament, and asked if he would take a look at our situation. Stefan was willing to give it a try.

The itty-bitty essential part arrived the next day. Stefan replaced it with a surgeon's skill and two hours of concentration. We turned the inverter on. The red light stayed off and my stomach stopped churning with nervousness—for an hour, until it came back on. *Shit.* I went to retrieve Stefan. There was another little itty-bitty even more specific circuit thing he needed to add to what he had already done. It worked. We were back in action, and able to water the farm, as well as benefit once again from all that the gift of power provides.

We had installed lightning protection and wired the system to code, but shit still happens. We could have chosen to be grid-intertied or even on the grid, but shit still happens and, while in those cases someone else holds the responsibility for repair, you are often, well, 'powerless' in such situations. Nowadays, the story might have had a different element of suspense given the plethora of solar companies and technicians within reach. But we wouldn't have had the experience of a mini-crisis, creative conversations while seeking solutions, the most human sensations of fear, hope, and, finally, relief. We would not have praised the importance of good neighbors. A sudden trip to the Jersey Shore would have likely resulted in some fine stories and a new tattoo, but this tale of perseverance and good neighbors lasts as long *and* doesn't fade.

Several years later and in the midst of winter, we would remain 'power-full' while hundreds of thousands were without for weeks. Ricky decided to do something he almost never does—he left the farm for eight days to participate in a meditation course in Vermont. He had been gone about four days when the storm hit. Our son Levi and I awoke to inches of ice on every tree and surface. With my hearing compromised from too much exposure to rock concerts, African dance, and Buddhist drumming—and hearing aids out for the night—I hadn't heard the pelleting on the roof and trees going down during the night until I awoke at dawn to what sounded like a war zone.

"Do not leave the house," I said to Levi, then nine, as I bundled up and headed out to survey the damage, especially hoping all of our farm greenhouses were intact. Trees had been cleared around those greenhouses to allow for ample sun, so fortunately none had fallen and crushed any buildings. I continued up the driveway to the road, hearing distant explosions—the sound of trees and giant limbs cracking and falling all around. I turned and headed back to the house quickly, not wanting to leave our kid an orphan with me under a tree and his father oblivious to what was going on, deep in meditation somewhere in Vermont without a phone.

Power was out for all of our neighbors and for about a million people throughout southern New England. But not for us. In fact, the next day dawned cold and sunny, as did all of the subsequent days that week, and into the next week, when utility grid-reliant electrical power for most remained out. Off the grid, with our modest array of photovoltaic panels, it was perfect solar charging weather. We had a full battery bank. In fact, we had more energy that sunny cold week than we could use. We welcomed neighbors who needed water or a shower. The back of our van, outfitted with a solar electric system, was kept open. Folks could stop by and plug in their cell phones or battery chargers for flashlights. In our resourceful neighborhood, folks managed to carry out basic life functions and cook on their wood stoves. But in most of the small cities nearby, the emergency shelters were full, with basic meals provided from school kitchens and generators keeping the lights and heat on. The impact was serious and the inability for most residents and communities to provide for basic human needs without electricity was striking.

The power eventually and slowly came back on in New England after the ice storm of 2008, and things returned to normal. There is a false sense of security that we will always be able to fix an energy crisis. At some point the power may not go back on and we will not be collectively prepared, as witnessed by the major disruptions and tragedies that continue after the magnitude of hurricanes now experienced and intensified by climate change.

Our home and farm are not completely off-the-grid. A small amount of liquid propane gas is used for our cooking. Energy efficient, on-demand hot water comes from a heater connected to a solar hot water system. Because we need to refill the LP tank infrequently, one summer day we ran out. A call to the gas company brought more. It also

Visitors like these UMass students experience off-the-grid living as well

brought the technician who must run a check on the tank when it is emptied. I came home from errands to a farm intern reporting that the technician had informed him that our water heater was broken.

"What do you mean, broken?" I asked the technician. It had been working great the day before, and for years before that. I explained to him that it was not kicking on because the solar-heated water entering it was sufficient. His face registered impossibility. "Feel this," I suggested, as I turned on the hot water tap, and steam rose from the stream. He left with his tail between his legs.

Living off the grid is not always easy, but the power of energy independence becomes startlingly real in situations like the ice storm, and is overall accompanied by a greater sense of security. It's also a way to demonstrate that a beautiful life can be had without over consuming fuel and contributing to global warming. Visitors have asked if it is a sacrifice to live off-the-grid. We have thought about this, about how the word 'sacrifice' shares a root with 'sacred.' Powered by the sun and with a modest array of panels—albeit increased to accommodate watering needs as we added more greenhouses—we have to be more aware of each day. The day length and quality of light, often providing more energy than we can use, informs how much watering or vacuuming, power tool use, or laundry can be done. This, in turn, serves to put us more in touch with these activities. Compared to the work of indigenous water protectors at Standing Rock resisting pipelines, environmentalists like Berta Caceres in Honduras who was murdered for defending her Lenca people against a massive, displacing hydropower project, and others who risk their lives daily on behalf of the earth, our sacrifice is nothing. Our increased awareness of the power of a star is quite a gift.

## Another Beautiful, Broken-down Night

It was a lovely winter night, cold and clear with fresh snowfall. We were full with the beauty of a Charles Neville concert at a local coffeehouse, having peacefully soaked up the music while baby Levi slept on our laps. Our friend Dan needed a ride home so we all loaded into our thirty-year-old Mercedes, tank full with the appropriate winter blend of biodiesel fuel. We cranked up the heat as high as it would go (not very high) and headed down the dirt roads towards Dan's house, roads we knew well from our years of gathering sap and making maple syrup together. Then the car sputtered and died. This was not the first time. Ironically, in our efforts to find an alternative to finite fossil fuels, we often found ourselves stopped in our tracks by the very fuel that we hoped would be a viable alternative. At this time in the mid-nineties, figuring out how to power a vehicle was proving much more difficult than installing solar, which was on the verge of a market and rebate program boom. Finding biodiesel, a vegetable-based fuel, as well as the rare affordable diesel vehicle that was not constantly breaking down, was proving challenging.

Our first barrels of biodiesel were sought after reading *From the Fryer to the Fuel Tank,* the funky, seminal book that helped launch the modern day resurgence in using vegetable-based fuels in diesel engines. Though the engine design hatched by Rudolf Diesel in the late 1880s was able to run on a variety of fuels, fossil fuel profiteers, who apparently didn't want that self-reliant secret to get out, overshadowed this information. The vegetable-based fuel movement of the mid-1990s involved two options: converting the diesel engine with the addition of a second tank and heating system to thin the vegetable oil, or the use of biodiesel, already processed to go right into the existing diesel engine (straight in the warm season, or mixed with fossil fuel diesel in the colder months). Both approaches reduced emissions substantially and forecast a future of regional re-use of waste vegetable oil. And, biodiesel could also be used in heating systems. While we personally used wood for heat, we were glad when a few fuel oil companies began to carry biodiesel for furnaces. We drove to Burke Diesel in Charlton, Massachusetts in our old pickup to buy the first barrels for experimentation with our Mercedes. We even got a gift of a logoed baseball hat (and later a visit) from Dennis Burke himself, happy to have us experimenting and spreading the word in Western Mass, which we did. Spreading the word later allowed him to be able to make bulk deliveries to us and others. At the time we thought we could check off another goal in regards to reducing fossil fuel dependency. We didn't realize how much of a multi-year and constant experiment it would actually be.

The good news was that biodiesel had solvent properties and would actually clean out your fuel tank and engine. The bad news was that the only vehicles we could afford were old and had a lot of built up gunk in the tanks and other engine parts. And so, that night the car sputtered and we edged as far as we could onto the bank of a snow-covered dirt road before stalling completely. This was an example of crud getting loosened and lodged into one of several fuel filters in the car. This filter happened to be underneath the old Mercedes wagon, and we were not going to crawl underneath onto the icy cold, rutted road with only a few stars as shop lights. Besides, we were lost under the hood of a car. On that cold, beautiful, broken-down night we got out to walk. Levi was sleeping in a blanket in our arms. We had long underwear, wool socks, and warm boots. Dan and Julia's house was not too far and had a fire in the woodstove. We had one tow still left on our towing plan (many had been used for similar scenic break-downs already that year). We would enjoy the walk and stars, and deal with it the next day.

As it turned out, we would deal with it for several more years and a string of subsequent vehicles—a Ford F-350 farm truck, an old Econoline Van, and even a newer VW Golf, the family car that replaced the old Mercedes when the cost of fixing the heating and other systems exceeded the value of the buggy itself. We tried the Greasecar system on the van for something new and different, and because this served as the 'SOL Patrol,' our roving educational van. Meanwhile, we successfully sought biodiesel from more local sources while we (and many others) awaited the completion of a large-scale biodiesel plant by an energy co-op who perhaps bit off more than they could chew. It is important to note that while we faced many mechanical challenges experimenting with vegetable-based fuels, it cannot be blamed so much on the fuel as the fact that Rick and I are both pretty inept and disinterested when it comes to tinkering with things mechanical. We are very clear that we like building things and growing things, but not ingenious about engines and other arrangements of moving mechanical parts. Fortunately, lots of other people are. We got to know some great auto shops in the area. But there are only so many times one can ring up big charges on a credit card in the name of experimentation, especially while making almost no money while growing our farm and nonprofit. We learned that so long as a fuel transition rests on the individual and without the infrastructure to support it, lasting change remains an effort of the determined and adventurous.

Years later, even with Big Oil's continuous attempts to kill the electric car, it is heartening to see options for high mileage electric cars and charging stations spreading. There is a hopefully bright future in terms of technology and interest. As I write, we are driving a modest, simple car that has hauled quite a bit of compost and mulch hay to local gardens while we save up for an electric vehicle and solar-powered charging station for such, as our off-the-grid house and farm system will not meet the need. Other ideas in the works are a shared solar electric car charging station in our neighborhood. We couldn't be happier to see more and more electric cars on the roads and in driveways, and hope that more renewable and energy efficient public transportation continues to evolve. We hope that soon we will be able to bop around in our own electric transportation when needed, and enjoy long walks on clear winter nights simply because it is a lovely, not a necessary, thing to do.

## Talking Turkey about Toilets

Many years back we were at Ricky's sister's house in Connecticut, hanging out around the kitchen counter where she raised her three kids and divorced her first husband, getting ready for Thanksgiving. The turkey we had brought, raised by our friends at Diemand Farm, was in the oven preparing to commingle on the buffet counter with many Baruc family traditions: artichoke dip with mayo and breadcrumbs, sweet potatoes with marshmallows, and canned jellied cranberry cut with a knife that makes cool ridges in the slices that you get to use only once a year. As I opened the cabinet next to the refrigerator to get crackers for the artichoke dip, I spotted another turkey. It was the kind that third graders dutifully complete by coloring in the feathers on the turkey's Native headband and writing what they are thankful for on the turkey's belly (a most bizarre perpetuation of the glorification of a dominant myth, and with genocide casually omitted). Our niece Allie had written in her bold, new cursive: "I am thankful for my family. And I hope there are no more starving children. And that my Uncle Ricky and Aunt Debbie get enough money so they can buy a real toilet."

Cracking up, I realized that it was easy for this eight-year-old and most of our other family members to miss our intention in having a composting toilet. Ricky's elderly father had grumbled a question several times during our house construction: "How much would it cost you to put in a real bathroom?"

"We're fine JB, this is a choice," was our reply.

"What is it, about twenty grand?" he insisted on knowing.

"It costs the water cycle, JB."

"What the hell is the water cycle?" He was perplexed and unmoved.

Around the world, women and girls are the ones primarily responsible for feeding their families and gathering water, sometimes spending hours a day doing so. While first world moms might stop at the market after a long day at work before picking up a kid up from school, millions of women are returning to their village home or refugee camp with the critical ingredient for cooking, washing, and hydrating to ensure their breast milk doesn't run dry. Precious water carried in a clay jug on their head or a leftover vessel reclaimed from a USAID project, perhaps lifted from a village well resounding with the gossip of the day. Here, too, in rural counties in the heartland, women are most often the ones running water from their tap knowing that the gas wells for hydro-fracking are leaking into the earth that feeds the waters on which their family or farms rely—but they have no other option.

We are blessed to receive our water from a 270-foot-deep well. It was beautiful to follow that water dowser around our land as his work-calloused hands gently cradled a forked branch that sensed water far below. The water that rises from our well is clear and pure. When we began to create a life on our land, the well was one of the first infra-structure pieces. Before we had the funds to put up solar electric panels, we affixed a hand pump to the top of the well casing. Ricky would get his daily bicep workout pumping for an hour while I held the end of the hose over tiny lettuce seedlings. While the solar electric system has long enabled us to turn on the tap, it still feels like a miracle to have it flow. We taste the sweetness whenever we return from places where the water is chlorinated or mineral-rich. Indigenous people throughout the world give power to the phrase "Water is Life," and so, our resolve to conserve and treat this precious cycle with care is strengthened.

That is why we don't shit in our water and then flush it away to a septic tank. When the tank is full, the water would be sucked out, brought to a sewage plant, and treated with chemicals and microbes before being discharged into a river, to then make its way back through evaporation to the earth, more polluted than before. That is why when someone raises the lid at our house, there is a pile of woodchips to which they add after using our composting toilet, rather than a white bowl offering up a pool into which to defecate. Our teenage son is not crazy about it, but he understands. Outside, 'humanure' composted for many years has filled the holes of fruit trees when they were first planted. Like most of what we do, the ideas are not new or original, but rather very old and time-tested.

Our friends and mentors Earle and Hilde, ever on the path of eco-logical sanity and creativity, created an eco-toilet center in Falmouth,

Massachusetts. Locals can learn that providing homeowners with an alternative would eliminate the need for a multi-million-dollar new treatment facility that would ultimately still dump feces-polluted water into the bay of this beach community. Their work and our work becomes increasingly interested in separating out urine, making 'humanure' even more compostable while reclaiming this vital resource rich in nitrogen and phosphorus. The Omega Institute where we teach channels all the water on campus—from low-flush toilets, showers, and the kitchens through an Eco-Machine (designed by New Alchemy co-founder John Todd). Up to 52,000 gallons a day of domestic sewage is purified as it moves through an aerated system rich with plants and microbes.

In recent years, we have especially realized the great benefits of urine. While the general population is not yet talking about this in the same way that we do fossil fuels, "peak phosphorus" is a critical issue. Essential to plant growth, phosphorus is a non-renewable resource that is being steadily mined and depleted. Urine is rich in phosphorus. It is sterile, and adults produce between 100-150 gallons of urine each year. This contains enough fertilizer to grow nearly a whole year's supply of food, according to the good folks at the Rich Earth Institute in Vermont, who are researching methods for safe and effective urine reclamation.

We now save our urine (as we are healthy and take no medications). Urine is generally free of pathogens, making collection, storage, and re-use quite safe. We have a container that is connected to our waterless urinal, plus discrete five-gallon jugs into which we offer our golden contributions throughout the day. Diverting urine from our composting toilets reduces any smell significantly. Filtered through a massive, layered barrel with wood chips clad with beneficial microbes, our urine is transformed into a fertilizer that we can spray on foliage such as garlic greens and seedlings. We witness their remarkable growth from this free product that keeps the nutrient cycle close to home. Once urine—and the valuable nitrogen and phosphorus contained within—enters the waste stream, it is hard to reclaim. Reclaiming it at the source can become an easy and natural part of the day. When we show visitors the odorless jars of nutrient rich 'microbe juice' that emerge from our simple urine digester, they are impressed.

Our relationship with the Rich Earth Institute has blossomed into an exciting step for the North Quabbin Garlic and Arts Festival, which has achieved a sustainability goal of 10,000 people diverting urine in specially designed portable toilets. Through festival committee member Bruce's diligent work with the departments of agriculture and public health, that pee, instead of being lost into a tank of blue liquid and ultimately to riverside 'waste treatment' plants, was applied onto the festival hayfields and others across the border in Vermont to fertilize land, and in doing so, fertilize hope for closing the nutrient cycle rather than flushing it away.

## Solar Solidarity

Ten minutes before landing in Baltimore I suddenly felt sicker than I'd ever felt. I was sicker than when I'd collapsed on the floor of a hut at the base of Annapurna miles from nowhere in the Himalayas, and sicker than the food poisoning I'd gotten from mayonnaise in a Havana hotel potato salad. The seat belt light was on and we were descending quickly towards the airport when I barged out of my seat towards the airplane toilet and emptied the contents of my stomach while the stewardess banged on the door for me to return to seat 8D. After deplaning, I continued to move through a haze, dragging my useless self through the next forty-eight hours, drained of all strength and mental capacity. Meanwhile Ricky somehow managed our large backpacks—one on the front of his body and the other on his back—and maneuvered one young child and a large and fragile package en route to an indigenous community in Costa Rica. Our family vacation replete with a mission to gift solar panels to a mountainous tribal education center had begun. Fittingly, we had planned to visit the new Museum of the American Indian in Washington, D.C. to start our trip. I spent the time pathetically groaning and sprawled on a museum bench while Ricky and Levi explored.

By the time we arrived in San Jose the next day, I was mostly better. We met up with Jose Carlos and Leila Garra and passed on the photovoltaic package for a youth center in their home community of Boruca in the Talamanca Mountains. We planned where to meet up with our new friends a week later to travel to their village. The panels were to provide light for the groups of young, indigenous leaders who met at the mountaintop center, built in traditional Borucan design. As the village elder, the ninety-four-year-old father of Jose Carlos had guided the harvest and construction of local timbers and reeds for this sacred gathering space.

When we first thought to go to Costa Rica, Ricky had asked if we could seek and visit an indigenous community. We knew it was a country known for "pura vida" and had been without a military since 1948, but we'd heard little of the native people. While researching our trip, an Internet search led me to Kan Tan Finca and to Jose Carlos and Leila, who responded to my passable Spanish e-mail with a warm welcome.

When people hear 'Seeds of Solidarity' they often think we are a seed company. While we do sell garlic seed, our name is mostly a metaphor for our intention to connect and ally with those locally and globally, and diverse in culture, language and lands. In this spirit, we wanted to make an offering as guests in their country. We did not know for a while into our time with them that Jose Carlos was a revered elder who represented Costa Rican indigenous communities at many international conventions. When they came to visit us years later, Ricky pulled from our shelf a book called *Basic Call to Consciousness*. In it was a photo of Jose Carlos as a young man in Geneva in 1977. He was with other indigenous rights leaders, appearing before the nongovernmental organizations of the United Nations to present position papers describing the oppression of native peoples in the Americas. Also having led an impressive life, Leila was a midwife whose work with indigenous women to retain their traditional diets as a means to prenatal health was documented in her book *Saberes y Sabores de Boruca*.

On our drive with Jose Carlos and Leila to his native village of Boruca, we took a detour to purchase a battery and some wiring that made our gift complete. Upon arrival, Jose Carlos brought us to the home of a local indigenous farming family, where we would spend the night for a few pesos—his way of introducing us to the village and a little support for the family. Grandma was grinding corn out in the back.

When Ricky motioned to join and help, she fell into rollicking laughter before letting him lend a hand pounding the corn for her fermented corn mash liquor. I went inside to say hello and give some small gifts to the children, who were gathered around a small screen. It was the winter of 2007–2008 and Barack Obama was running for President. We watched and listened over the TV's static. After a few minutes, with the kids realizing I spoke some Spanish, a girl of twelve or so looked me in the eyes. "¿Él es Marrón?" "Sí, " I said, "es verdad." Yes, he is a brown-skinned man. This was something they could not believe. It was something Ricky and I could not quite believe either. We spent several nights in Boruca. We helped install the solar electric system and were welcomed into Jose Carlos' extended family that included a birthday for his elder and wise father. The solar electric system gave light, but we are sure we received more from their glowing warmth than they did from our modest gift.

When we were seeking a solar electric system for our home and farm in 1996, it required a lot of time and research to make it happen. Even ten years later, getting the panel and supplies to bring to Costa Rica was a bit of a project. We did not know then that we were on the cusp of a solar revolution of sorts, that many of our friends would install grid inter-tied systems, and that solar farms would spring up to both joy and controversy. Many years later we would be proud that my Bronx-raised octogenarian parents would be among those installing a photovoltaic system, and proud of their choice to leave a little more sun energy and a little less impact on the planet to the next generation. We would not have guessed that our neighbor and long-time dairy farmer George Hunt—who, while making a delivery of composted manure to our farm pointed to our panels, asking, "do those things really work?"—would later install a system on the entire length of his cow barn, as well as over a large expanse on land that had only previously grown rocky outcrops.

Calculations along with differentials in resource consumption vary by country, but consider that most countries could power themselves with solar electricity using less than five percent of their total land mass according to research by Finder.com. Then there are the benefits and potential of small-scale wind power and hydroelectricity implemented in ways that do not destroy ecosystems or communities. Yet internationally, governments provide at least $775 billion to $1 trillion annually in subsidies to the fossil fuel industry—not including other costs of fossil fuels related to climate change, environmental impacts, military conflicts and spending, and health impacts. That is a lot of money that could be used to support small-scale, decentralized, renewable energy, mitigate the impact of global warming, and create jobs.

Over a billion people worldwide still live without electricity, some much more contentedly than those of us who have become overly dependent on it. In terms of equity and justice, those of us who consume more of the world's dwindling and polluting fossil fuels must use less, and transform our ways through conservation paired with renewable energy as we increase access to community-scale renewable energy. From Costa Rican indigenous communities to a long-time dairy farm a few miles from our own solar-powered vegetable farm, may we move towards a future that is bright with solar solidarity.

## *Field Guide for Chapter Three*
## *The Sacred Sacrifice: Living with Less is More*

## Questions to Ponder: Source and Resource

- Do you know the source of your water? Where does your waste go? What and where is the source of the energy/power (for electricity, heat, transportation) that you use? Who is involved in these, and what is the impact on their lives?

- All humans have an impact. What is one, relatively simple daily change as well as one long-term change you can make towards increasing energy conservation and/or transitioning to a 'cleaner' energy source, reducing water use, and minimizing waste?

- Does the idea of 'living with less' feel empowering, challenging, or both?

- Are you aligned within your relationship and family about energy use, waste, and related lifestyle choices? If not, how can you reconcile these different choices?

- Who/where are current groups, resources, and businesses that can help you navigate how to reduce consumption and waste and transition to renewable energy sources?

## Down to Earth: *Do It Yourself*

### *Depict your Energy Lifestyle*

*This activity increases your awareness of both what you use, and what you may actually need.*

On a piece of paper, write the words 'Energy In' and list or draw the (categories of) ways in which you use energy and natural resources in your daily life. These might include: powering your home (electricity for lights, appliances, work, entertainment), heating and cooling, water use (drinking, bathing, laundry), storing/preparing/cooking food, and transportation. Depending on your style, you can make a graphic bubble that contains each, a table, or lists under each category.

On the other side of the paper write 'Energy Out,' and depict the types or categories of waste you produce, such as pee and poop, greywater (used, non-toilet water from dishes, bathing, etc.), your garbage (trash, compostables, and recycling), and emissions from fuel use.

Next, to the best of your knowledge, for each category of 'Energy In' add the actual sources of energy for each (perhaps in another color). For the 'Energy Out,' identify where this waste product goes.

Look over what you have created: a depiction of your current energy lifestyle. In which categories do you feel you are already conserving to the best of your ability? For example, for transportation, you might already use a bicycle or public transportation. Or you may already compost all of your food scraps. In which areas do you feel most compelled to shift towards a more ecological footprint? Add a dollar sign to those that require some money to change (even if there is payback and money saved in the long run), and take note of those that don't require any or require very little. For example, installing a more efficient hot water heater might require some initial cash, whereas diverting your urine from the waste stream to transform into fertilizer costs nothing.

What additional information or support do you need to help you make a transition (rebates, resources, grants, or simple equipment)? If you don't have any ideas, do research, as there is a lot of information out there!

Prioritize the categories that you feel most excited about shifting. Create a goal for two or three, along with a manageable, doable timeline.

## Awaken the Power: *Contemplative Practice*

### *Meditation on Sustenance*

This can be done as a sitting or walking meditation as you wish. Consider one source of energy that you use to power your lifestyle. For example, oil or wood for your heat, propane or electricity for your cooking stove, water for so many things (and certainly, the sun or wind if you use these already).

Identify and then contemplate the natural resource that is this source. Envision the actual source of this resource. Allow your mind to wander to the landscape from which this energy is being extracted or produced. Consider all those involved in the labor of bringing this to you. You might envision those who work on a drilling rig in Texas, uranium extracted from aboriginal lands in Australia, a coal mine in Kentucky, the local logger who cuts your wood, the driver who delivers your propane, or a deep well or reservoir of water that gets to you through gravity or some form of electricity.

Allow yourself to feel whatever arises based on what you see in your mind's eye and feel in your heart. The intention of this is to deepen awareness of the sources, lands, and people impacted by our energy and resource use. It might feel painful; the impact is real. It might feel beautiful as you increase connection to source. As you breathe, generate gratitude for this resource.

Coming out of the meditation, consider (or share with others) how it felt to do this meditation. How might you emotionally, spiritually, or creatively increase awareness of and respect for this resource?

## Ten Ways To Practice Simple, Daily Acts of Gratitude

- Face the direction of sunrise upon waking and wash it over yourself.

- Let the first words out of your mouth be something kind.

- Pay full attention to your breathing for at least five minutes a day.

- Consciously touch some part of the natural world each day: soil or snow, a plant, water, or wind.

- Shape a gentle smile for softness and an open heart.

- Send a wave of love to two people during a pause in your day— one for whom it is easy to do so; the other, not so much.

- Prepare at least one of your meals each day; share food you grow or prepare with family, friends, or those in need.

- Know the source of your food and energy and the path of your waste. Change something you do or consume in the direction of reducing your impact on the lives of others and the earth's finite resources.

- Make or do one thing that involves creativity every day.

- Before you sleep, thank whoever or whatever you believe participates in the creation of life, no matter how hard or good your day has been.

# Chapter Four

# Cultivating Hope, Educating for Change

## *SOL Rises*

Road trips for teaching have always provided time for envisioning, assuming Ricky isn't tilting his head back in the passenger seat and nodding off after a particularly tiring stretch on the farm.

In the fall of 1998, we were on a road trip to Cape Cod in our old silver truck to visit friends and harvest bamboo for trellises when we came up with the name SOL (Seeds of Leadership) Garden. We had begun to envision our first education program and now this impromptu naming ceremony propelled our hope to create a garden-based program for local teenagers on our land. We were in our mid-thirties, excited, and had a lot of energy and sufficient accumulated experience (and fortunately, minimal fear or foresight about what it would really take) to plunge into not only expanding our farming and building our home, but also into launching our first education program, starting a festival, and having a baby—all in the same year.

My work with youth and school gardens had begun at New Alchemy, where I'd helped grow the garden education programs for neighboring kids and schools. While living and farming in California for a year, I had called an organization called Life Lab Science and was quickly placed as a volunteer at a great little public school, with equal numbers of white hippie kids and children of Mexican migrants who worked the artichoke fields that extended to the sea. As it turned out, I was not only the volunteer but apparently also starting the program. I enlisted several community organizations to come together on a Saturday and dig the beds, build a fence and tool shed, and teach the Life Lab classroom activities. I was not quite twenty-one and no one else was in charge, so I got to play leader and start my first school garden program.

Upon return to New Alchemy, I remained connected to Life Lab as I helped grow the New Alchemy garden education programs, deepening my understanding of how to weave gardening into the public school curriculum to teach science skills. Although educational philosophers like John Dewey had long ago touted school gardens as essential living laboratories, the now strong movement was in its early days, and I was called on through the 1980s to offer Life Lab trainings to schools up and down the east coast along with my dear friend and school garden comrade, Kim. In addition to foretelling what was to be a focus of my career, my literal experience in the field strengthened my application to Antioch New England's Environmental Studies program as a non-BA special admissions student. As a multi-tasker who also needed to make some cash while in school, I sought out an internship the same day I was accepted to Antioch. That internship then became a job with the Hitchcock Center for the Environment in Amherst, Massachusetts. I taught science and environmental education in the Amherst schools, then pitched a position providing environmental education field trips for Massachusetts Migrant Education, and then was asked to stay on and run the bilingual hands-on science enrichment program in the Holyoke schools, which I did for several years. Shifting between English and rudimentary-to-conversational Spanish, I developed an environmental education curriculum that I taught in the elementary schools in this community of Puerto Rican, Irish, and French Canadian residents. Teachers in one school were especially interested in garden beds as part of our program together. These garden beds became a central focus of the program.

As these school gardens continued to grow, so, too, did my commitment to uniting the fields of multicultural and environmental education. I continued on to the doctoral program at the University of Massachusetts, given the opportunity to work with a national leader in Multicultural Education, Dr. Sonia Nieto. With her amazing mentoring and exposure to peers and teachers, I completed the program. My dissertation research focused on urban, culturally diverse youth who were active in environmental issues in their communities, entitled *Youth Spirit Rising,* homage to the passage in Martin Luther King's famous and radical speech "Beyond Vietnam." This organic progression through education and experience would lead to our first and ultimately flagship educational adventure at Seeds of Solidarity—but how to start?

While exploring our new community, I had seen a flyer at a nearby general store announcing an anger management group for girls. I called the number on the flyer and spoke to the director (and then sole staff) of Quabbin Mediation, Sharon. It turned out we had met in other circles years before. My experience as a yoga practitioner and teacher was forefront in my mind when I offered to volunteer. But after I'd taught the first yoga class, Sharon and I began chatting about our interest in creating a garden-based program for teens in our new community, where there was no shortage of need to guide youth towards positive activities.

We wrote and received our first grant in partnership with Quabbin Mediation. We also created a memorandum of agreement stating that the program vision and name Ricky and I had conjured on our road trip would remain ours once we formalized Seeds of Solidarity Education Center as a nonprofit organization. The grant received was from a state agency that focused on substance abuse prevention. In retrospect, knowing how challenging the grant world can be, this was really lucky—if not divine intervention. It provided two years of modest funds for materials and a teeny wage that enabled us to get things started. Most of what I remember about our first grantor was a program director named George who, perhaps contradictorily (though much appreciated), showed up with a bottle of homemade wine to drink with us program leaders after his site visit.

We had eight youth the first year of SOL Garden. This wasn't bad considering we had no pictures of years past or stories from SOL alum to tell their peers how great it was. Most were referred from an anger management program and so they sort of had to come. We met every Thursday after school through the spring, then all day in the summer months. We started a garden at the far end of our farm, and designated the space and the acre around it "SOL Garden." Ray Hendricks was in that first group of participants. I never knew what he did to get himself in a mandated anger management program. As one of the few young black men in the predominantly white, working class community, racism was surely a factor. He was smart, creative, and exemplified the kind of outside of the box thinkers that we hoped the program would attract. We had charged the kids with coming up with a program slogan. One day out of the blue, Ray—then an aspiring musician—suddenly chimed in with "Food for the SOL," which remains the motto to this day.

Once our first grant together ended, we revisited the memorandum of agreement and set off on our own to form Seeds of Solidarity Education Center Inc., a 501(c)(3) non-profit. This statement makes it sound easy, but it was not. It was worth the energy, the wait, and the paperwork. It was not easy to set off on our own, largely because our partner had gotten attached to the program too, and didn't want to let it (and us) go. Fortunately, that story ends well because we remain organizational allies and I later joined (and later became president of) their board of directors.

Each year we expanded the SOL Garden area on the far end of our land. The numbers of participants grew, as did our relationships with the schools. We did our best to communicate thoughtfully with school administrators, and kept raising funds and showing up year after year—even in one school that initially gave us the cold shoulder before eventually warming to our perseverance. We learned that doing something modestly that grows over time is more successful than promising the moon for one year, then disappearing. It helped that youth were returning to school from our program with strengthened confidence, leadership ability, and improved grades.

In the early years of SOL Garden, youth and staff raised a green-

Local teens who participated in the first decade of our SOL Garden program inspired us to do it for another ten years.

The initial mission statement remains: 'To inspire service and activism among North Quabbin youth as they use their bodies, minds, and hearts to cultivate food and a hopeful future.'

house, designed and built the 'SOL Shack' meeting space, constructed a tool shed, and built a water-pumping solar electric system. They dowsed a well, made art, song, and performance, donated thousands of pounds of vegetables, and created gardens for others in the community. The first program t-shirts featured a logo made by SOL Gardener Kacie (who later became a farmer, then teacher) to match the slogan innovated by Ray, who became a successful musician. They've felt and spread kindness and compassion, shared pain and healed trauma, and been supported by adult mentors and their peers to take paths towards a brighter future. They've spoken at food justice conferences near and far, and I've swelled with pride over their heartfelt words. I've written innumerable letters for their first-generation college applications and job references. Many have their own children and feed them fresh vegetables that they learned to grow at Seeds of Solidarity. Two decades after inception, well over 450 young people and thirty interns seeking experience to ripple its teachings outwards have gone through SOL Garden. We could not know the magnitude of our scheming in that original truck ride—or what a long, bountiful trip it would be.

## *Flying Greenhouses and other Farm-to-School Adventures*

"Can anyone name a farm near where we live?" I asked while teaching a lesson on local foods to third-graders in preparation for the school garden we would soon create with them.

"Cumberland Farms!" replied one enthusiastic boy. This, for anyone not familiar, is a convenience store. It is not a farm. It is one of two in our town, both in walking distance for most residents. A grocery store is not. Some assume that if you live in a rural area, kids will know and have experiences with the land. While there are many connected to farms, hunting, and fishing, many children in poor communities like ours experience a great deal of transience and trauma.

School gardens should be integral to the curriculum of every public school for the valuable cross-curricular possibilities they offer. There would be increased access to fresh food for (often hungry) students and families, healing, cooperation, and a host of other things. They can be challenging to integrate and sustain. While there are a few well-funded celebrity chef school gardens across the nation that receive acclaim, there are thousands of teachers, food service directors, parents, school nurses and community activists around the country that have created gardens at schools by pulling a few bucks of seed money out of their own pockets.

In the first decade of Seeds of Solidarity programs, school gardens and farm to school initiatives were a primary focus. Thousands of kids thrived on farm-to-fork experiences through many a school garden adventure we knowingly or unknowingly created.

To prepare for the first greenhouse we built at an elementary school, we had followed all of the right protocol—or so we thought. We'd met with the teacher and principal. We had looked over the schoolyard with the custodian, and agreed on a spot that was also easy enough for them to mow around. The greenhouse components had arrived and were waiting in our garage, funded by a USDA Community Food Projects grant we'd received to fund this and six other school gardens, greenhouses, and related workshops for teachers and students. To get a jump on things before putting screwdrivers into the hands of thirty fifth-graders, we spent a day prepping, digging, leveling, laying out and securing the 12-by-14-foot frame foundation for the greenhouse. All was good. We were ready, kicking back at the end of a long day. Then the principal called.

"We had to move the greenhouse foundation," he said. I couldn't imagine I heard him right. "We realized we forget to check with the sixth-grade teacher, and put the greenhouse foundation on top of his simulated archeological dig."

It was already evening; we were due to return for a day of building with kids early the next morning, and I did not sleep well wondering what we were going to return to. Fortunately, the principal was a handy guy. He and the custodians had moved it all without too much destruction. After a little patching and re-leveling that morning, the class bounded out and by the end of the day, their greenhouse was ready to receive the first of their seedlings that waited patiently on the windowsill, ready to see the light outside.

That was the precursor to another school greenhouse project the same year, the one that almost disappeared, not due to disinterest but to a wild wind that sought to ungraciously re-locate the structure to the adjacent athletic field. An experienced group of middle school teachers were excited to integrate the greenhouse project into their project-based approach to teaching. On a beautiful spring day, groups of kids worked in teams to assemble the greenhouse. Their sense of ownership was palpable. Those challenged by middle school math in the classroom impressed their teachers at their ability to thrive with hands-on experience and a few tools. Finally, near the end of the day, the structure was ready for the glazing—a large sheet of plastic—always best done on a calm day. Then the bell rang and the kids begrudgingly headed back inside for their afternoon classes. As the supportive principal walked by to check in, we explained our student-less dilemma. He returned ten minutes later with a guidance counselor, school nurse, maintenance person and another unsuspecting staff. Together, we finished the days' work, with the added benefit of additional school staff invested in the project. While the structure was secured to the ground, apparently we had underestimated the wind tunnel on the chosen site. A few days later, some strong winds picked up. They also picked up the greenhouse, the glazing acting as a kite. The students didn't even think to ask for a pass to leave their science classroom as they ran out the door, chasing their beloved greenhouse. Repositioned, repaired and secured, it provided many seasons of salad greens, seedling sales, and summer crops.

Another of many memorable school garden ideas was a marathon event in celebration of Massachusetts Farm to School week. We would plant autumn salad greens totaling the number representing the year, 2008, at six schools in one day. Farmers know that 2008 seeds is in fact not an outrageously huge amount but, to a second-grader or even a sixth-grader, this sounds—and is—pretty exciting. The morning of the well-planned adventure it was pouring. My right-hand gal and education program coordinator at the time, Kaitlin, showed up well suited in rain-gear. She had learned early on that at Seeds of Solidarity, the show pretty much always goes on. We inventoried and packed up our tools for the day: hand-held seeders, an assortment of cold-hardy seeds, and a clipboard for each school with pre-printed sheets for students to count the number of each seed planted and total them. We added a thermos, lunch, and change of clothes, and we were off. Our muddy boots immediately began dripping on the floor of my car that thinks itself a truck (with good reason). Seeds of Solidarity had worked hard to earn the reputation for always showing up, and this day was no exception. Teaching kids to show up and endure is a good lesson, too. Three elementary, two middle and one high school later, we had met and exceeded our self-imposed challenge, engaged hundreds of kids in the process, and linked math to the garden-based program. We did not look anything like celebrity gardeners Michelle Obama or Alice Waters. We looked like drowned rats that would contract a head cold for the next few days. I extracted a moist spinach seed packet from my rain jacket pocket, no longer impermeable to the day. There were just a few seeds left. I offered them to the land at my feet.

In 2006 and at the height of our farm-to-school and school garden efforts, public school districts nationwide were federally mandated to create and adopt wellness policies to promote healthy food and physical activity. Per typical bureaucracy, no extra funding was provided. The night I pulled into the parking lot of one of our town's elementary schools for a school board meeting and saw all the cars, I figured there was a special event. I didn't realize that the masses were there for the meeting, and that the presentation on the new wellness policy was the special event that the hoards of PTO parents were there to see. But I did know that I was the presenter, which was in that moment a personally intimidating realization. I entered the meeting and walked past a line of PTO mothers. They eclipsed the hard plastic chairs meant for second-graders, their arms folded across their chests in a confrontational position. They were there to fight to keep their bake sales, whatever it took.

Our closest ally was the amazing school food service director named Sherry Fiske, who had deep roots in the community. Sherry made her rounds to local farm stands to pick up whatever was in season well before anyone was using the term 'farm-to-school.' She'd fold fresh spinach or kale into breakfast eggs and lunchtime soups, make applesauce, and freeze berries and store squash for the winter ahead in order to get local fruits and veggies into the bodies of the 800 children for whom the free breakfast and lunch at school were often the only meals they would eat that day. We had worked together to expand the school garden she started, plus start more at three other schools in town. Sherry worked closely with her food service staff to bake from scratch, inspiring them to chop and dice fresh veggies rather than open cans. Without any fanfare or well-researched reports on waste reduction, they simply had the kids scrape their few leftovers into a slop bucket picked up by local farms to feed their pigs.

Often, farm-to-school advocates have to deal with resistant food service staff and insistent parents who, suddenly outraged when they realize their kids are eating crap, become activists only as long as their kids are in school. In our community, roles were interestingly reversed. With Sherry in the lead, school food service was on board, but many parents were not. The Friday bake sale was an institution. This hallowed day featured whoopie pies, marshmallow Rice Krispies, and boxed vanilla cake oozing with pink frosting—all before lunch. Classes won prizes for making the most money at the bake sale they were assigned to host. Kids and parents got excited when they made good cash at a bake sale, as it meant another bus for kids that otherwise might not get to Sturbridge Village or the Boston Aquarium, ever. Now a wellness policy designed in Washington, its designers having never stepped foot along the abandoned mills of our community, arrived to threaten bake sales—as well as imply that what these families ate was probably not okay either.

I did my best to explain that this policy was something everyone across the country was facing, and tried to emphasize how many good things we already had in place in our community. The bake sales wouldn't necessarily need to go—maybe change, but not go. We could decide that together. But at this time, too many kids were hungry, in need of exercise, and nutrition impacted their learning—and we had a responsibility to address that in our schools. A few women shifted slightly in the second-grader seats. Their arms relaxed a little.

A short time later and with the help of a grant Seeds of Solidarity received to help local school districts collaborate on wellness policies, we held a sit-down dinner in the school cafeteria, complete with table linens and lots of local fare. In collaboration with my friend Kelly Erwin, founder of the Massachusetts Farm to School program, we invited and achieved a mix of superintendents, teachers, health educators, school nurses, food service staff, parents, local physicians, community organizers, students, and farmers representing six school districts interspersed at each table. We invited the PTO parents from that tense meeting, and some came. The conversations at the tables were rich with ideas. As important as the process of crafting policy was the power of sharing a meal over conversation, for our children and communities.

Sherry Fiske, food service director extraordinaire, retired soon after. She needed to focus on healing from the cancer that was discovered—a Stage IV sentence that her goodness, sincerity, and dedication could not ultimately stop. She outlived predictions by five years. On a rainy April day, about three months after Sherry died, sixty friends, family, and teachers gathered in a circle to plant a peach tree in her honor at the school where she offered so much nourishment.

Sadly, her farm-to-school legacy was thwarted by the hire of a misogynist jerk who couldn't care less about fresh food. He uprooted one of the gardens as soon as he was hired. Furious, I unleashed upon him and the hiring superintendent a verbal rampage. It was simply too hard to work with him; I eventually needed to move on to other projects where gardens could flow with ease. Fortunately, district restructuring meant his tenure was short. Another food service director arrived who was not like Sherry (few could be!), but who still sought fresh and local whenever possible.

Over the years we have tried all kinds of things as part of our commitment to create and sustain gardens and related programs at schools

locally. We have spread what has been learned to hundreds of teachers throughout New England. In addition to the many raised bed gardens and several greenhouses, we held seedling sales and mini-farmers' markets where kids voted to use proceeds towards purchase of fresh local fruit for the free summer lunch program. We created mobile cooking carts with a blender, hot plate, assorted bowls, utensils, and recipes to inspire young chefs to prepare fresh food right in their classroom. We prepared feasts of cornbread and squash soup, pizza and apple crisps and invited parents to the feasts. In addition to working with schools, we provided food preparation and cooking classes for kids living in low-income housing, at summer free lunch sites, and with a local YMCA where youth learned to prepare fresh, healthy recipes. They then composted all of their plates and food scraps.

There are a few things we learned and continue to convey. Small is a beautiful way to start and much better than a grandiose plan that gets out of control. Let your project grow from successes. One small garden tended by one class will build admirers and momentum. The other main lesson is to find and make allies. The school custodial staff is too-often overlooked, but they are the ones who care for the land, and often have the longest tenure as well as gardening knowledge to respect and draw from. Finally, think creatively and specifically about how the garden can meet academic and civic goals of the curriculum. This is critical to school gardens being seen as integral, not extraneous—although, in truth, shifts in administration and ever-changing educational mandates make long-term sustainability a challenge.

My vision of education includes the opportunity for every young person to connect to the soil and water that sustains us, experience culturally appropriate ways of growing and preparing fresh food, and practice civic engagement as they make meaningful contributions to their community. Given that it is rare for garden-based learning to be integral to school culture, I've wondered if short-term experiences of hands in the earth through a school garden matter. The words of a fifth-grader from one of our programs will always warm my heart: "I will probably have a big garden...really big, so everyone in town could come and garden and take away what they need...that would make fresh food part of everyone's life."

## Strong Women, Power Tools, and Backwoods Dudes

The day was over, almost. We still needed to pick up and deliver a truck-load of compost and soil to bring to the other end of town so we'd be ready to create a garden for Cherilee and her family the next morning. As most people were sitting down to dinner, we were hoisting twenty-five heavy barrels of a compost/loam mix into the back of our truck. Riding slowly up North Main as the sun prepared to set, we had some sweet time on the bench seat of the old F-350 to check in about our day.

"Where are we going again?" asked Ricky. This became a standard question preceding our weekly Thursday evening soil delivery during the years that we created a raised bed garden each Friday from April to June for families in need of fresh food. It was a program we named Grow Food Everywhere for Health and Justice.

"You'll see soon enough," I said, having visited Cherilee at the decrepit cabin in the far reaches of our town a couple weeks before.

If you were shown a photo of the scene that you might assume it was in Appalachia, not Massachusetts. In a state where images of colleges, Cape beaches, the Berkshires, and Boston dominate, you don't expect places like that day's destination, unless you live in the North Quabbin and know that they can be found here. Pulling in the edge of the dirt driveway, the television blasted out beyond the torn screen of the front door.

"I'll just stay in the truck," said Ricky as he looked cautiously out at the tar-papered cabin tacked onto a trailer bordered with bags of trash and a rusted truck.

"Thanks a lot, keep the truck running, would you?" I said as I pushed aside the pile of farm invoices and toolbox ever on the truck seat.

I had called and tried to reach Cherilee to confirm our arrival a bunch of times earlier that week. I never got through. Like many in our community, she bought phone time by the minutes she could afford. But, we had set a date to put in her garden that Friday, and our motto is "we always show up." So we took our chances, in ways that were appearing to increase as darkness fell. "Hello?" I called as I approached the door. Nobody came out. I knocked, still nothing. I looked back at the truckload of soil. I was not leaving with that load still on it. I was out of my comfort zone. My vivid imagination played a split-second mental movie that featured a rifle poking out of the door of this backwoods camp. I took a deep breath and walked around to the side of the trailer where I could see the TV glowing through a small window and a hulking man resting on the couch. Above the sill and below the bottom of the vinyl shade was framed a hairy belly bulging out of a tee shirt. "Hello, it's Deb with the stuff for the garden," I bellowed quickly.

"Huh? Oh, wait a minute," I heard, as the couch creaked with relief and he met me at the door.

"She's not here," he said, in a voice softer than I'd expected.

"We just wanted to unload the garden soil for tomorrow, sorry to bother you," I offered, gesturing towards Ricky and the truck to reassure us both.

"No problem, over there is good," pointing towards a spot right near our truck before returning to his couch.

The next morning, I arrived with my young intern, Catherine. Thankfully, Cherilee was there. So was Randy, as we learned was the name of the man I had encountered. Cherilee got on her phone, apparently reinstated with enough minutes to summon a nearby pickup truck with a bunch of young cousins in the back, who jumped out to help move the barrels and wood for the garden to the designated spot in the back. Cherilee's four-year-old Dakota was the most enthusiastic, insistent on carrying the large drill case. She had only one forearm and hand, the other missing from birth.

Cherilee had openly told me that she was an addict, now sober. Her pregnancy had helped her get clean. We laid out the wood where they wanted the garden. Grasping it with her one hand, Dakota leaned into the mighty 18-volt drill and put in several four-inch hefty screws one after the other, stopping only to begrudgingly give her brother and cousin a turn.

I think they enjoyed the garden that summer. Cherilee had told me that her father was dying, and her putting in a garden was in part for his love of plants. She told me that she too loved vegetables (and ate them right out of the can). Her garden was tender in more ways than one. Like many of the other twenty raised bed gardens we created for families with great need, things change rapidly due to the often-uncertain lives of people living in poverty. Jobs are lost, landlords evict, homes are foreclosed, relationships split, children are removed, and drugs take people down. The least of these problems is that the garden is left behind to grow only weeds. Sometimes we'd pass a home where there was once a garden, seemingly no longer there, then be pleasantly surprised to run into the recipient who'd had friends help load all the soil and wood into a borrowed truck to move it with them to their next rental. Creating gardens for low-income families had been a vision for a while, and we were finally able to get a grant to pay for materials, staff time, educational workshops, and garden manuals for twenty families over a two-year period. Experience taught us some things that blossomed into a related and stronger program.

During the years that we put in gardens with and for economically struggling families, we partnered with several local social service agencies to help get the word out to potential families. While strengthening our ties to area agencies as well as through conversations with the families in our Grow Food Everywhere for Health and Justice garden program, we learned more about the local subculture of women who run home-based childcare, and serve as a center of stability and constancy within the tumultuous lives of many of the families they serve.

What can you do when you are a rurally isolated woman who starts having kids young, doesn't have opportunities for college, and wants to stay home and care for their own children rather than seek

Intern Catherine and youth leader Nicole ready the lumber for the garden that soon filled the spot to their left along with...

one of the limited and limiting night shifts at one of the few remaining factories in town? The road to becoming a family childcare provider might start by getting a few bucks from a friend to watch their kid while you are watching your own. Then you take some courses, get licensed, and increase the numbers of kids you can care for at one time. You get an assistant, and join the local childcare provider's group that meets monthly to share ideas and activities. Through that, maybe you get connected to the system that enables you to accept vouchers from families who qualify based on financial need, or fill out the paperwork to receive reimbursement for providing meals that include wholesome foods. You continue to take night and weekend courses. Now you are a woman who has her own business—sometimes the mainstay of the family finances—who has gained an education in early childhood care, and who has peers in the community. You serve families for whom you are a trusted caregiver, not to mention a source of parenting and life counsel. And, unlike at K-12 schools where the day schedule is often tightly dictated and with frequent administrative and curriculum fluxes, you have the self-determination to incorporate the garden into your childcare program in ways that are creative and consistent.

...neighboring single moms and abundant veggies.

Our Grow Food Everywhere childcare provider program launched each spring with a workshop for the providers filled with activities, good food, and connection. They left that workshop with a date for their garden implementation or refresher, a set of colorful hand tools, and a colander garden to demonstrate growing greens in small spaces to keep them enticed until the May date when we arrived with wood and soil for their raised bed garden.

While cedar is a great, naturally rot-resistant wood to use for raised garden beds if you can afford it, we didn't have that kind of budget. Instead, we purchased locally harvested rough-cut boards, usually hemlock or pine, from a local mill. The two-inch-thick boards make for a sturdy garden frame. We pre-cut the wood for our standard 8-by-4-foot by 16-inch-deep raised beds. These dimensions allow for a nice array of crops, as well as use of vertical space and things like cucumbers and nasturtiums cascading off of the sides. We don't recommend shallower beds as they are not deep enough for crops like tomatoes, and the soil compacts and needs to be replenished after one year of use. That said, the beds we make do require a lot of soil—about 1.5 cubic yards, our preference being 50/50 ratio of finished compost to loam. To further build community connections, the youth in our SOL Garden program contributed by readying the garden wood with a non-toxic, whey-based stain to extend the life of the wood, and helping to raise the seedlings we would gift the women.

Similar to the approach with our Grow Food Everywhere program for low-income families, on the appointed day at the childcare site everyone helps: two-year-olds, the providers, and the occasional parent. Within two hours, a garden frame is built, cardboard laid on the bottom, the barrels of rich local compost/loam mix dumped inside the frame (mostly) by teams of toddlers with an adult helping hand. The first of the spring seeds—peas, carrots, beets, radishes, and salad greens—are planted.

We created gardens with twenty low-income families first, and then in the years following, with an additional fifteen women who run childcare programs. Program insights enabled us to share best practices with hundreds of other early childhood educators across the state. Here is how it multiplies: one garden at one family childcare site reaches ten families at any given time. The childcare providers in our program that insisted "I tried to garden and it doesn't work for me" are now avid gardeners, expanding their garden with more raised beds, containers, and anything they can find. They've put overwintered spinach on the table for the lunches of kids in their care, let the little ones graze directly from a patch of colorful lettuce. These kids learn they actually do like tomatoes when picked from the vine, not the supermarket. Many parents report that their kids "love veggies more than junk food" and that they are inspired to start their own gardens in containers for now, and at their homes when they have them. One provider who said she once couldn't get anything to grow worked with her husband to wrap four more garden beds around their outdoor play area. They feed their own four kids as well as the twelve or so in their childcare, and host a container garden workshop for the families they serve. The women all say they will continue to garden as part of their childcare programs.

We went by Cherilee's place not too long ago. The trailer and house had been taken down. Driving by, I couldn't see if the garden was still there from the road—but I remembered that time. The night we almost backed out before delivering compost for a new garden makes for a good story. But the ones about the women who care for hundreds of children and their families every day, year after year who now put their own garden produce on the lunch table are way better.

## *Waking up from a Coma*

"I feel like I am waking up from a coma," she tells me, while kayak paddles dip in and out of calm water. As we go slowly up the Miller's River that cuts through the center of our old mill town, Anita speaks of being sober after forty years an addict, living on the street, working in prostitution, and losing her kids. She's never kayaked before but is gliding through the smooth surface near the reedy edges intuitively. She would say the same words the next morning as I pulled out the yoga mats and she tried it for the first time.

"You are a natural," I say, holding back my tears as I consider all that she has seen as well as lost.

Anita and two other women arrived on a Saturday with our friend Annie, a long-time recovery counselor, as well as artist and all-around cool person. When Annie first came to one of our Solidarity Saturdays and described the container gardens she kept on the stoop of the Worcester Suboxone clinic where she worked, we knew we'd do something together.

Our simple goal of the retreat for these women in recovery was to offer them a little beauty, kindness, and food from the land. Annie later told me that when they arrived and saw me holding three small bunches of flowers they asked her why. "I think they're for you," she said. And they were.

Annie had extended the retreat to three women that she felt were ready and would hopefully not relapse, at least during the thirty-six hours at our place. Anita was longest sober, over a year. Elena, German-born, looked the part of a businesswoman who finished her work day on the treadmill, but this image faded quickly as she showed the photo of her young daughter, removed from her custody, who she repeatedly held up as her reason for getting clean. Lori had owned her own beauty salon, but the makeup she wore well did not cover the sense that she was holding on to the edge of a terrible cliff. "I never thought this would be me," she said. Prescribed painkillers were the start of her journey into hell and she was still there.

We drank tea, harvested beans and tomatoes from the gardens, and made art with Annie. We prepared dinner together and then ate it outside by the grapevines. Over the fire that evening we had s'mores, laughing and talking. Conversation meandered towards the pharmaceutical giants, and their hold on medical doctors and on the public. These women had the most straightforward analysis I'd ever heard.

We are farmers, not addiction specialists, but this epidemic needs everyone's attention. We live and work in an economically depressed rural area hit hard by the opiate crisis and we want to do what we can to insure that teens especially know that life holds much more for them. 'Brian' was only twenty and we'd known his family since he was in preschool. When I went into science classes to talk about our SOL Garden program, Brian was one of the few students who responded when I asked a question about ecology, agriculture, or climate change. He often took an application, but never applied. He played baseball and couldn't do both. He stopped in one summer day a year or so after he graduated to show his girlfriend our place. They were just out driving around and he wanted her to see it. We didn't know he'd been paying attention to what we were doing at Seeds of Solidarity, but he was.

His mother later told me it was Percocet for a couple of years, but heroin for only seven weeks. One night he got a text and a fix. At 3:30 in the morning his father found him blue and gone. Anita woke up, Brian didn't. He had gone fishing with his father the day before, told him he was definitely turning over a new leaf. At age sixteen, our son Levi went to the wake with his soccer team, Brian's brother being a teammate. It was an open casket. His mother told me kids needed to see.

The genetically modified seed pushers and Big Pharma drug kingpins have some things in common. Companies like Monsanto push the theft and control of seeds. They infiltrate the soy fields of the Midwest, the corn of the Maya, and the cotton of farmers in India, many of whom have committed suicide as a result of being pulled into debt wrought by terminator seed technology that makes growing these crops impossible without the herbicides purchased from the companies responsible for this technology. Meanwhile, the pharmaceutical industrial complex pushes painkillers that can lead to fentanyl-laced heroin, available for an eighth of the price of prescription pills on the street. Over-prescribing and misuse are critical issues that have escalated since 1999, with fluctuations. According to research by SAMHSA (Substance Abuse and Mental Health Service Association) carried out in 2015, almost 200 million Americans aged twelve or older (close to 45 percent of the population) had used prescription psychotherapeutic drugs in the previous year (inclusive of pain relievers, tranquilizers, stimulants, and sedatives). Of these, 20 million were considered misuse. There are some excellent organizations, medical professionals, and people in recovery who actively address both over-prescribing and addiction, but societal responses that promote whole-person, community-supported healing are also vitally needed. True health care should include nourishing food, meaningful work, restorative leisure, and value the power of loving relationships and the importance of kindness and community. Health care is when people are taught the skills for their own wellness and resilience in order to live full, self-determined lives. Freedom from the corporatization of our food supply goes hand in hand with freedom from a pharmaceutical system that both feeds on and promotes isolation and disconnect for profit.

With decades of experience growing healing food, we thought we might be of service to those in need of healing. As nearby Heywood Hospital prepared to open Quabbin Retreat, a day and residential center to serve adults and adolescents struggling with addiction and mental health challenges, we reached out to them. We have learned that positive partnerships can move with individuals as they move among organizations. We had worked with Dr. Rebecca Bialecki when she was director of our local community coalition, and she was now Vice President and Chief Agent of Change at Heywood Healthcare. Our history together paved the way for conversation and ultimate collaboration.

Quabbin Retreat was a beautiful and already healing space in which to envision therapeutic gardens, as it had for many years been a Sisters of Assumption Monastery. We received a grant from the Heywood Healthcare Charitable Foundation that enabled us to design and implement a path consisting of nine stations with names like Scents/Sense of Hope, Awaken Taste, Gratitude Garden, and Shine Brightly, as well as accessible raised vegetable gardens. We developed accompanying contemplative activities to be used by a therapist with a group, or in a self-guided way to unite breathing, yoga, writing, mindfulness, and meditation with the different themed gardens, and created colorful signs throughout the garden to guide these. For these, we located reclaimed cedar and had it milled into posts as well as flat boards that we lettered (at home, before installing) with commercial grade paintmarkers and a clear, long-lasting finish.

To implement the gardens we proposed an all day community workshop to build and fill raised bed vegetable gardens and plant perennial patches for the healing path. While it is always our philosophy to engage stakeholders in projects to build ownership (and because it is fun!), this also supported the 'good neighbor' goal of Heywood Health-care, which was sensitive to the concerns expressed by some community members at the arrival of recovery center in their small town—even though it might come to serve their own family members.

As it often does on our workshop days, it rained. And as it often does when we have a deadline to haul large quantities of wood and compost, the truck broke down (fortunately just after we managed to haul over most of our materials). We created the gardens just before patients arrived in order to be sensitive to confidentiality. A hardy group of Quabbin Retreat clinical and grounds staff, hospital volunteers, and local community members joined in. We introduced the cardboard method as a great way to make perennial gardens lower-maintenance, placing cardboard covered with natural wood chips around all of the plants, which had been put into holes enriched with local compost. The raised wooden vegetable beds we built were of local, fairly inexpensive rough-cut lumber that we stained with a nontoxic whey-based finish to extend the life of the wood.

At the end of the day, we were very muddy and the gardens very beautiful (and well- watered!). As patients arrived, many found great joy and meaning in the gardens, as well as some unplanned ways to build community, as described by our project partner Rebecca Bialecki:

> The timing of the garden coincided with the start up of the Retreat's programming. Daily, and weather permitting, the garden was used as a closing part of the day, to support reflection of the day and each person's individual path to recovery. One participant that was particularly involved in the maintenance of the vegetable garden was ready to complete his treatment program. Although he was very pleased with his progress, he expressed concern with leaving treatment and asked if there were ongoing ways to stay involved. The staff was able to identify a small group of participants that were ending their treatment to bring some of the vegetables grown to the weekly Farmers' Market on the Common in Petersham. They attended with a Care Coordinator to answer questions and to let people know about the program. This was an invaluable addition

to treatment in that it allowed people to feel that they were giving back, and to begin to feel more valued by their community.

I returned one day in fall to do some work on the signs while a group of day patients were exploring the gardens. One young woman with huge circles under her eyes looked distantly familiar, and was perhaps even a short-term SOL Gardener; another was a dad-looking guy clad in UMass swag. One young man was clearly in the midst of his pain, and would only sit distantly from the group with his hoodie clouding most of his face, eyes lowered. I spontaneously did a few minutes of yoga with them—hands to sun, to heart—before offering some sprigs of rosemary and lemon balm, sage and mint to inhale and taste, bringing a sprig to the shrouded young man perched alone on the stone wall, who would reach out to take it without eye contact.

I thought back to Anita and the other women in recovery arriving at our farm a few years prior, and how we'd watched her blossom with each hour and touch or taste of something green or colorful on the farm, and sent a prayer of hope that the healing power of plants would make it so for many in this quiet but powerful garden.

## From Septic Field to Spiritual Garden

We first visited the Omega Institute in Rhinebeck, New York in 2009, which was also the year they opened the Omega Center for Sustainable Living (OCSL). The centerpiece of this green building was a Living Machine biological treatment facility into which entered all of the black- (poop/pee) and greywater produced by the hoards of healing-seekers that populated this former Catskills summer camp from April to November. We were taking part in a postseason treat to ourselves: a workshop with Pema Chodron. During a workshop break, we went on the weekly tour of the OCSL with Omega CEO Skip Backus. He was not the guy in a suit we expected, but a smart, funny, down-to-earth man who had run the Omega facilities crew for years before rising to this position. His reverence for nature was authentic, palpable, and necessary for the project that he oversaw, and which lay before us: a series

We bring the farm to Omega—seedlings and symbols of good food for all form the center of our workshop circle...

...to be planted in learning and unity.

of subsurface constructed wetlands where microbes and plant roots cleansed the wastewater from all of Omega. Before going to Omega, we had taken notice and seen pictures given that the designer was our friend John Todd, co-founder of the New Alchemy Institute, a visionary so pivotal in our own lives and direction.

The tour was great, and the meditation teachings and workshop were just what we needed to regenerate for the winter ahead. In his heartfelt and fluid fashion, Ricky hand-wrote effusive gratitude notes in the margins of our most current Seeds of Solidarity newsletter, leaving a copy for Skip and a program developer we had met there before we headed home. Embedded within was something along the lines of "we love what you are doing here and we'd love to teach at Omega."

A month or so later we got a call. They were, in fact, just designing a series of workshops to complement the OCSL project, and would we be interested in teaching? Over the winter we sent in the needed course description, photo, bios, and contract. "What do you need for a garden space for hands-on teaching?" they asked. We replied that a simple plot to work with would be fine—nothing special—along with a nice stack of corrugated cardboard, a few bales of mulch hay, and some compost. And, nothing special was what we got!

We arrived for our 'Grow Food Everywhere' teaching weekend a few hours in advance of our course in order to investigate. We unloaded the wood we'd strapped to the top of the car to build a demo bed and started to pull a few trays of seedlings out of the back. Then we saw the furry ones. Peril number one: groundhogs. They were all over the grounds and brazen. They were so brazen that in the Omega central garden (more sanctuary than production), every single plant was imprisoned in wire fencing. It was the only way, we'd heard, to protect them from the fat little nibblers that waddled across the paths. The seedlings stayed in the car.

Next we checked out the spot they'd allotted us to create a garden with the group of thirty signed on for our course. We were excited to teach, and confident that they'd be so inspired after our weekend together that they'd go home and start a bountiful garden of their own. We pulled a shovel out of the car to take a scoop of soil and check it out. Tip in the center of the area that would soon be a garden, Ricky gave the shovel a little weight with his foot. No movement. Nothing. Like rock. We pulled a small sledgehammer and piece of rebar from our tool stash in the back of the car. *Pound, pound* he went, and the rebar moved maybe a half-inch into the ground, but no more.

No-till, no kidding. There was no going down into this ground at all. In fact, there wasn't much grass on this open field. In fact, this was not an open field, but an old leach field. We looked around. To one side, an old tarp hung over a small bench nestled into a few trees, a coffee can on the end. A couple of guys walked over and sat down and we realized that hidden from the lavender-scented guests, this is where the seasonal staff came to smoke. We waved, knowing this garden would be, in part, for them. We looked back to the barren spot that we were charged with transforming. The requested cardboard and compost had arrived: thank you to the angels that are the maintenance crew. And on the other edge of the field we spotted some piles of leaves, brush, and scraps of wood. We could work with this; we had to.

Years after that first effort at transformation, the area boasted deep rich soil, and several raised wooden bed gardens, the handiwork of participants in each annual course. And, after many years of us leaving precious heirloom plants and seeds there and knowing, with some frustration, that the human caretakers might not get much food after the woodchucks had their way, Omega provided us with another spot, almost as lousy land-wise, but professionally *fenced* as well as adjacent to the Center for Sustainable Living to serve as inspiration for those on tours.

We still teach this course. The course circle opens with names and a movement that illustrates a food that brings them joy, nourishment, or healing, as well as sharing what they hope to gain for their lives or community by taking the class. We then move through many ways of growing food, health, and resilience, from urban steps to suburban lawns to small farms. We create a beautiful garden together in a sacred time rich with community building and continuity. We've had nutritionists who realized they had no idea how to grow the food they prescribed, dedicated and diverse urban elementary school teachers, psychologists, suburbanites, neuroscientists, war veterans, young seekers, and international activists from Puerto Rico, Guyana, and India. One of our closest connections was made with Stella and Malik—months after he died suddenly in a car accident we would unload a crate of course supplies and find his 'Grow Food Everywhere' nametag in a spot it had no reason to be other than to be a message to remember from a beautiful man on the other side. The gardens now hold many years of the energy of participants, as they laid cardboard, hauled compost, painted prayer flags and built beds and benches together. Our class would be one of the first in Omega's sustainable living track, and later a part of the four-week Omega Ecological Literacy program. More than a gardening course, we bond as we build, create, and consider how to bring a garden revolution into each life and community.

## Green Drinks, Orange Jumpsuits

We stood in Tadasana, the Mountain Pose. We rooted our feet to the earth and reached the crowns of our heads upward before sitting back into the chairs circled on the grass wet with morning dew. I closed the few minutes of yoga in our circle of twelve, Sun Salutations culminating in this final balance position. Seemingly simple, the stillness of Tadasana can make for an internally challenging pose, but the men in this circle had become well practiced at stillness. They ranged in age from twenty to sixty; some were incredibly fit, others not at all. But everyone had willingly moved their hands from heart, exhaled down, lunged one leg at a time back, extended into Downward Dog, and arched slowly into Cobra without complaint or resistance. As we sat, Ricky opened the cooler we brought and poured everyone a cup of green drink, made that morning from our farm's kale and spinach, thickened with some banana, sweetened with maple syrup from our land. The men in the circle dried their dew-moistened hands on their pants before receiving a cup.

Their pants were all the same orange cotton. There were no shoes to replace on post-yoga bare feet. Everyone wore Velcro sneakers, and removing them had not been an option. Some sipped the green drink slowly, others quickly. All waited considerately for Ricky to round the circle again with seconds, as a guard stood on the circle perimeter, politely nodding *no, thanks* to the offer of green drink.

I felt the sun on my back as it rose over the concrete building behind me and noticed many of the men lifting their faces instinctively to meet it, some for the first time in months. They sipped, receptive, as the vitamin-rich drink nourished spaces which had been recently filled with much less healthy substances.

It was our first of five classes in an organic gardening course for which the men would receive college credit, along with other classes on food preservation, forming cooperatives, and creative writing. It was also part of our county jail's efforts to include fresh food produced on site in the meals served to the men, and initiate programs for their families to benefit as well. And, it was the first time such a course was happening in medium- rather than minimum security. Most of the men in this pod were there for drug-related crimes, and for some, the disease of addiction was co-occurring with mental health issues.

Everyone checked us out at first—the men, the guards, the program directors. I would have done the same in their position, especially if I was among the incarcerated. What did we know about being where they were, other than having to relinquish our wallets and other personal possessions to security before entering? We would leave after a few hours and receive a thank-you on our way out. They would be searched before returning from the razor wire-bounded yard to their cells. We were allowed to bring things in, but had been cautioned on what was not permitted. No paper clips—they could be used to pick door locks. Gardening books we brought as gifts had to be checked to ensure there was no contraband tucked in the pages.

Inside the gates, arranged and prepared by garden coordinator Joshua, a stack of local lumber was cut and ready to build into four raised garden beds that would then be filled with a mix of local compost/loam. We would make these with the men over the coming weeks along with weekly lessons in sowing seeds, soil health, and natural pest control. We were approved to drive our car into the yard filled with our usual crazy array of tools, buckets of compost, containers of seeds, and trays of plants and seedlings. Our old car went through two gates and two guards before we parked it inside. When I once had to move it away from the mound of compost during class, I was keenly aware of the men wheeling around to hear the key being turned, a simple act unless you have not turned your own key in years.

Ricky and Joshua had decided on a garden bed fastening system that utilized screws that could not easily be removed from the beds for other purposes. I was impressed that they were letting us bring in cordless drivers. My sometimes overly creative mind had already conjured a few "what if" scenarios. These definitely never happened. What *did* happen was that several of the men—tradesmen and business owners before falling to addiction then crime to support their habits—looked us in the eyes and thanked us, for they had not held a tool in years, and tools had been an extension of their hands and their livelihood.

Shaun looked like a typical contractor who might have shown up on a crew for a job at my parent's house. Michael reminded me of our son's friends; he was an athlete and A-student who, in his words, took some really wrong turns. Paul remembered us, said he'd helped build a greenhouse with us at his middle school and visited our farm on a class trip. We had read an article about Kevin in the local paper before we knew we'd be teaching at the jail. He had been running the treadmill for exercise, and found that being cigarette-free in jail had enabled a capacity to go and go. Inspired by a prison counselor who was a runner, he decided to run the Boston Marathon from within the concrete walls. He borrowed a slightly larger pair of regulation Velcro sneakers to allow for swelling feet, and got special permission to have a water bottle. He needed to start earlier than the thousands of runners that April day in order to be back in his cell in time for head count. He completed twenty-six miles to the supportive congratulations of other inmates and staff, before heading back to his cell. We were happy to see him months after our course ended. After serving a five-year term, he was at an art show of work by those incarcerated when he told us he'd be running his next marathon as a free man. With court dates to make and transfers from medium to minimum security, sometimes guys we had grown fond of would need to exit the course without finishing. One day a student was absent from class. Nope, Jones won't be coming back, his peers told us, looking particularly dulled, having just spent twenty-four hours in lockdown while the contraband was traced to him.

Teaching this course annually goes down in Seeds of Solidarity history as one of our more unique experiences, replete with some of the most attentive students we've ever had. Each week includes a combination of learning, conversation, and experiential activity. Once we introduced the class-opening ritual of a green smoothie, they looked forward to it every week so we brought other things to taste, too. Once I made rhubarb sauce and local yogurt. I thought I'd sweetened it enough, but my sweetness barometer was clearly very different from those who have not only drugs, but taste buds assaulted by years of soda and donuts for breakfast. Over the course duration, we showed them how to sow and transplant, explored soil and no-till methods, and modeled ideas for container gardens they might make with their kids once they were out. A few old-timers had strong ideas about the virtues of Miracle-Gro and listened with arms crossed but an open mind to alternatives.

To create the garden beds that were central to the hands-on class as well as a much-needed physical energy release, some men helped construct the wood frames while others hauled compost in buckets and barrels from the waiting pile to fill the frames. We had the cardboard trailer unlocked and raided it to cover the sod below the beds. We laid some extra cardboard down to demonstrate the no-till method. When the class session arrived where we would plant the raised beds, we had them self-form small groups to do the planting. It really didn't cross our minds until they told us afterwards that it was a new experience to communicate together, let alone agree on the layout for a bed of peppers, tomatoes, and basil. We had just assumed that since they were in the slammer all day together and sometimes for years, they must talk. Not really, as it turned out, at least not in the way you do when you are making something beautiful together. And they were.

Our course officially ended just before the deep heat of summer kicked in, but the plan was that Joshua, the Garden Program Coordinator, would keep tending the gardens with some prisoners in minimum whose days held a little more freedom as they transitioned towards the halfway program before release. The first summer we made the gardens was one of extreme drought, and you can't have hoses in the yard. You can't have anything over six feet long that could be thrown over the razor wire and climbed up. But Joshua found a way to keep the mulched beds sufficiently watered over the months, filling buckets at a nearby spigot. One of the men in the class worked in the kitchen, which gave him the ability to enter the enclosed yard to bring things to the dumpster, so he was able to help water, too. The heat-loving crops thrived with the rich compost, days of sun and a backdrop of concrete walls. The Sheriff was a huge advocate from the start, and it was decided that the next year would bring the course again, a new circle of students, and four more garden beds. A small greenhouse built by Joshua sits where the pile of compost was. On top of that, we were asked to provide some cooking workshops—without using glass or knives—to unite visiting children with their fathers, a very tender experience in which I had to hold back tears while demonstrating how to make a dressing for kale salad and shake cream into butter for fresh cornbread. Together, they ate pizza topped with vegetables from the gardens and decorated cardboard frames for the photo mementos they would take—but for one man who spent the entire time with his eyes closed, holding and rocking his year-old baby boy.

We created the syllabus for the course before we had a sense of who our students really were or what they needed, and so designed gardening experiences for both time in jail as well as upon release, with hope they would carry it home to their families and for their continued health. It is known that excess leisure time without constructive activity is one of the factors leading to recidivism, along with lack of employment. While teaching, we tried to relate food and farming conversation topics to micro-business ideas that could make for meaningful, entrepreneurial work, from food trucks to small compost operations. An assignment for the last class was to share your idea. A few of the men even chose to work as a team. There was a pig farm that supplied barbecues, a composting operation, a market garden, and a roadside veggie stand. And there was a farm-fresh food truck serving green smoothies—they were over orange.

## Great Moments in Fundraising History: Migraines and Miracles

*Fine Homebuilding* magazine used to have this insightful section on the back page called "Great Moments in Building History." This is where accomplished builders told their stories of screwups, the unexpected, and opportunities to laugh at themselves. There was the story of the painter who used up their cans of leftover paints to create a primer undercoat, a great idea until the owner came home unexpectedly to a lilac-peach-mint barn. And the one about the builder who couldn't stand the sight of the pink bathroom fixtures in the house he bought. After a night out drinking, he smashed them to pieces, only to later realize it was just the lighting that made the beige fixtures look pink. These tales were not so much the recounting of construction woes but the honest, laughable stories of deflated egos and perseverance. They offered a re-minder to do good work and be creative, but also practice some level of non-attachment and maintain a sense of humor. We have found it to be the same with fundraising.

Our very first significant grant was successful, which is kind of surprising and also unusual in retrospect—if it hadn't have happened, would we have pursued starting a nonprofit organization? We partnered with another local and budding organization to write it as we didn't yet have our own nonprofit status, and it provided seed money for the first year of our SOL Garden program. We then initiated the process to incorporate a nonprofit organization, working with a lawyer under his reduced payment plan, which meant we did most of the work with his knowledgeable advice. That took about a year. We read some great books from Nolo Press on the process, but we were more focused on getting the 501(c)(3) status than thinking about the details of actually running and sustaining an organization. We stayed the course with the back-and-forth of paperwork with the IRS until we achieved that long-awaited, affirmative piece of paper in May of 2000.

We had no plan, training in, or sense of the realities of fundrais-ing. It was literally day-to-day, hand-to-mouth. With our great ideas and experience in the field, surely someone would be thrilled to send us a big grant, right? Innocent and bold, we started at the top, submitting an involved proposal to a food security program within the USDA. Not having any idea how to write a grant, I met with a recommended grant writer who was very experienced, but for some reason didn't advise us that with no track record, our chances of a big multi-year federal grant were pretty nil—or perhaps I just didn't listen. I couldn't manage to type into the budget forms and this was before better online applications were created for such processes, so I printed, then cut and paste—literally, with scissors and glue stick—114 sets of 12-point font numbers and painstakingly glued them into position on the budget sheets. I included a lot of pretty color photos even though they said not to, but how could they resist?

It was actually a really good proposal with ideas akin to what is now called a mobile market—but perhaps envisioned before the community food movement was ripe for such. We could have likely done the project described—by the skin of our teeth. But they didn't give us the chance to show that. The rejection was a wake-up call with a hearty dose of heartbreak. It solidified the realization for Ricky that he was not going to be able to put down his shovel and be at the mercy of funders for our future. He kept farming, and I kept writing grants.

We next wrote a modest one to the New England Grassroots Environment Fund (NEGEF) to create our very first outreach materials. We got this one. Designed by our graphic designer and good friend Lynne Rudié, we look back on and still really love that first brochure. One of the few remaining copies is framed, complete with a few tea stains. We took our time and had fun designing a creative and beautiful piece, and launched our dragonfly/sun logo as part of this. Excited by that first $2,000 grant—the first we had gotten on our own—we made the trip to the annual NEGEF gathering in Maine. It seemed like the right thing to do, to show up to be part of this network that had offered us support. Bill McKibben, not yet well known, spoke to the group assembled. At dinner, Levi, then not quite two, barfed all over the floor from the side of his high chair. Ah, yes, we were off to a roaring start with this good impression and connection-making thing.

Three years later we landed that USDA Community Food Projects grant, after a nice streak of several smaller ones from foundations. I took the call from the director of the program and went outside to look for Ricky, shaking with joy and relief at all that a sizeable, three-year grant would enable. It was timed perfectly to take our organization to the next step as we also grew our youth program, initiated six school gardens, and launched farm-to-school in our region.

Over the years to come, I learned to search foundation directories and wrote many grants from private and public sources, and got enough to sustain and modestly grow the organization. I learned that there are some magical moments, and you never know when you might be chatting up your organization with someone and they say, "You know, I have a friend who has a family foundation that might be interested...' We've encountered a few entitled donors who wanted us to do it their way (we learned to say thanks, but no thanks), and other foundations and program officers who really got the essence of our work and stayed with us for the long haul. From early on, we learned how important and nourishing it was to build a community of supporters. Each year during our annual appeal, we receive envelopes containing anywhere from five dollars from a low-income elder, to five hundred or more from those able to support with great generosity. It is our philosophy that every gift is valued, and we take the time to add notes to each outgoing letter to donors, and a card of gratitude upon receipt. This is our favorite part of fundraising, because those that believe in you stick with you over the long haul.

We've also had some super fun and often crazy events and fundraising ideas along the way, too, from Zydeco dance party benefits to stickers hustled at vegan restaurants in the Boston area, to selling hand-printed t-shirts along with our logo shirts at the Garlic and Arts Festival. One year Ricky even shaved a garlic design into his hair and allowed people to launch a water balloon at his noggin for twenty bucks. I think we made forty dollars total. Both participants were his brothers. The generosity of others has been super. A local disc golf course holds an annual snow bowl where players come out no matter the weather to benefit our organization and a local food pantry. Others might have multiplied their gross income, staff, and board members many times over twenty years, but we have a small-is-beautiful philosophy. And we're still here.

While we are not nonprofit management experts by any stretch of the imagination, there are a few things we have learned along the way and in the trenches.

- Stay true to your organizational values. Reflect and affirm these values and your mission in all you do, including organizational culture, programs, materials, and fundraising.

- Be sure your programs follow your mission. Do not start something you cannot finish, or create a project just to get a grant based on a timeline that may be irrelevant to community needs or which overextends your capacity. Modest long-term initiatives may be more powerful (and sustainable) than a short-term, grand splash project. That said, take some creative risks, too!

- Show up for other people's stuff, organizations and events. Then they show up for you.

- Feed your staff (and everyone): share nourishing food at events, meetings, and programs. Start meetings and gatherings with a circle to connect each other and ultimately strengthen your work.

- Seek allies in your community work; your best allies may come as a surprise and open new doors, connections, or resources. Stay receptive.

- Volunteers are great but not free. It takes time and energy to support and manage interns and volunteers well, and to meet real needs. Think through these needs, staff and volunteer time, and relationship-building with care.

- Being a nonprofit does not mean you need to give everything away or do anything when asked. Stay true to your capacity while meeting your mission. Boundaries and clarity help everyone.

- Remain resilient. Do not allow the image or reality of a room of strangers trashing your grant proposal to devalue your work. Endure rejection without anger or defensiveness. Carry on with focus and love.

- Believe in generosity. People do not throw money at your feet, but magic happens. Express gratitude often.

## *Twenty Years of Soul*

I did a rough count, and realized we have sat in eight hundred circles with youth in our SOL Garden program. Beginning with the first day of a new SOL Garden season in April, every weekly meeting starts and ends in a circle, which, over twenty years, makes about eight hundred, not including the times we circle to greet a guest presenter, or before we enjoy a summer lunch featuring garden-fresh food, grown and prepared by youth. If you add the fact that over 450 local youth have found themselves here, that is a lot of diverse tushies on the circled wooden benches on land that we have made available just for this program. While founding SOL Garden was a natural progression for me as an educator, SOL Garden looks a lot like a place I wish I had as a teenager.

Our community is low-income and isolated—geographically, culturally, and by poverty and trauma—and its youth reflect this demographic. It also has some of the most receptive young people I have ever encountered. We seek funding through public and private sources so that it is free to youth and families. Building relationships with public schools has been vital to the success and longevity of the program. We offer ecology-oriented presentations in science classes to hundreds of

students each year in order to turn students on to the idea of applying. Now teachers, guidance counselors, and former SOL Gardeners actively help spread the word too. It is a creative process from the start. Many months before the sprouts of a new season, we meet with our seasonal SOL Garden staff to envision the sequence of activities, things we hope to grow in the garden, as well as overall themes of the program to align with current community or global needs. If staff and interns have particular interests and skills, we incorporate those, such as our longest co-leader Jacqueline, who brings creative writing and an artist's mind, and Micky, who brings much knowledge of climate change and is a devoted naturalist. The SOL Garden season starts anew each April with a combination of returning youth—who we call 'mentors'—and new participants, ages fifteen to eighteen. All live in our region, but for most, the few miles outside the center of town to our site on the edge holds something new.

Many stories were created in twenty years of running a program. There was the time that our group was set to take a hike, but Michelle had sprained an ankle. No one would leave her behind, so we tossed a wheelbarrow in the back of the truck and the SOL Gardeners took turns pushing her along the trail, to great laughter of course (and luckily no more bruises). There was a young, essentially homeless couple who, a few years after they graduated SOL Garden but not quite high school, showed up at the Garlic and Arts Festival with a baby, no place to live, no money, and a very cute puppy that they said they couldn't keep. We could, and Topaz became a loyal and beloved part of our farm and family well into his old age.

There was the year we loaded up our 'SOL Patrol' biodiesel van with as many youth as would fit, along with all we needed to serve and sell burritos and salad at Solarfest in Vermont to raise money for our program while exposing them to a great event. Other journeys included flying young women with me to present at national community food conferences, and closer to home, Ricky taking some of the young men—many without or estranged from their fathers—on an overnight backpacking trip. There was Vanessa who journeyed on several powerful walks for peace after encountering the Peace Pagoda on a SOL field trip, and went on to become a member of the Seeds of Solidarity board of directors as well as our extended family. While it is not a farmer-training program (we reserved that for our farm apprentices), some SOL Gardeners have, in fact, gone on to farm. Others will simply but powerfully have their own garden and feed their children fresh vegetables.

One memorable spring it seemed to rain every other day. On a May afternoon twenty-five of us sat on our handmade benches formed into a big hexagon on the flattest piece of ground between the greenhouse and garden. The sky quickly grayed, then blackened. Each week at SOL Garden we start with an opening topic—food miles, fair trade, labels and GMOs, ecological pest management, climate change, nutrition and the like. That week the topic was youth activism. I thought something light and simple would be a good way to initiate the opening conversation as we passed the snacks. "Name a time you acted to help a cause or help someone out," I suggested.

I was thinking I'd hear "I made brownies for a bake sale / participated in the car wash to raise funds for band uniforms / picked up litter." But as often happens, sharing in our circle goes places unexpected and powerful. "I quit my addiction to alcohol... I helped my friend who was homeless find a place to stay... I supported a friend who was abused by her ex-boyfriend...I came out as gay." And the list went on as the circle went round.

I could feel Ricky and our staff member Carrie taking it in as we made eye contact and shared a silent expression of *Holy shit, where do we go from here?* And then the first rains started.

Grabbing backpacks, everyone ran for cover in the greenhouse, laying out some of our tattered blankets in a big circle on the greenhouse soil. The previous week a group of kids had removed the previous year's tomato cages and winter-withered vines. Not yet replanted, the greenhouse was our best option for cover. The space was dusty but dry, and dry was what we needed as the heavy clouds opened.

Inside, we tried to keep the conversation going, but intense rain hitting a greenhouse drowns out any possibility of talking. So we just paused and listened to the sounds. Then the first kid asked—"can I go outside in the rain?" It was warm, and there was no lightning, so why not? And then the next kid, and the next, until most were standing outside in the downpour, faces to the sky, arms overhead, waters running over them, cheap mascara dripping, sneakers mud-covered, t-shirts soaked. They were cleansing, this was clear: some in silence, others yelping with uncontrolled laughter. We watched them, all with something of our own to release and maybe heal.

Some people ask how we have gotten teenagers to want to garden and grow food. For some that might be the reason they are initially drawn to SOL Garden. After years of doing this, we have learned that, for most, it is the sense of community, the spirit of acceptance, and the opportunity to do authentic work and explore expanded worldviews that keeps them coming back. As SOL alum Cody expressed, "This place has given me the tools to feed myself, and the tools to not only heal, but grow. I was given the environment to ground myself and expand my reach and views in this world. The person I have become is a product of many things, but SOL Garden can be found all throughout my life."

We practice sharing and inquiry in our circles, and sometimes experience heartfelt expressions from the youth. Emily offered, "The sense of community has renewed my hope and instilled a positive outlook on how I view the world" and that "being surrounded by change-

Skills for self reliance, such as building, complement gardening. Creativity amplifies the message. Activism
translates to current issues. The season culminates with a SOL-ful booth
at our Garlic and Arts Festival, with
our Congressman and food justice
advocate Jim McGovern, a regular.

makers everyday inspired my mind views and my physical choices on a daily basis." Darnell dealt with moving through high school as a black teen in the nearly entirely-white school district. He was popular and well-loved, and well aware of school not being a place where deep conversations about social issues often took place. Darnell recalls: "SOL Garden changed my life in a lot of ways but the biggest way was by getting into college... you were the first person I went to for a letter of recommendation. It was the most influential letter I had received and without it I probably wouldn't have gotten in."

Clara is a musician who reconnected to her Native American roots at SOL Garden, with Ricky regularly loaning her books and magazines by indigenous authors. SOL offers many a much-needed place to be who they are, without judgment. A gender-fluid artist, Cat self-identified as having Asperger's. During their first year they did not show up for week two, and I was surprised as I thought they had really enjoyed it. When I called, they told me they had been suspended for bringing a penknife to school. They had been threatened repeatedly by another student and were scared. They returned the next week, then every week for three years.

We love exposing youth to the plethora of cool people we have had the opportunity to meet: ecologists and chefs, beekeepers and body workers, artists and social entrepreneurs. One July day we had a local singer-songwriter come as a guest presenter. Over an afternoon we had collectively composed a song to a blues rhythm that we later performed at our Garlic and Arts Festival. It speaks to the love, community, good food and soul that is SOL Garden.

## SOL Garden Blues

*Chorus:*

*I got the SOL Garden blues, and I'm cooking with Soul*
*I got the SOL Garden blues, and I'm cooking with Soul*
*Working together... is gonna fill the bowl.*

*Verses:*

*Start with love and passion and here's what you do*
*Come on over for some SOL Garden stew*
*With hard work and passion we can change the world*
*We've all got something so let's give it a whirl*
*Gather around... let's all come together*

*Respect for each other, Respect for the food*
*Respect for each other, Respect for the food*
*Holding hands together... we're gonna show respect for you*

*We plant love... Every step of the way*
*We plant love... Every step of the way*
*Harvesting soul... all night and all day*

*Together we work the fields, of open hearts and minds*
*Together you and I, will bond humankind*
*We'll build immunity... and start a strong community!*

*Field Guide Chapter Four:*
*Cultivating Hope, Educating for Change*

## Questions to Ponder: Programs and Partnerships

- What is an organization in your community that you admire, and why?

- What is a need or gap in your community that an education program, initiative, or organization (new or existing) might help to fulfill?

- Who are you most compelled to work with? (for example, young children, people with disabilities, youth, elders, survivors of trauma, etc). And who are the people or organizational partners in your community that are, or could be allies?

- What style of envisioning and bringing programs to fruition is most comfortable or interesting to you? Solo? Through partnership or a small group?

- What/where are some existing or potential barriers or resistance to change, and how might you prepare to navigate these?

## Down to Earth: *Do it Yourself*

### *Envision a Personal/Community Garden*

There are a multitude of methods and opinions regarding how to garden that can be helpful—but also overwhelming! Whether you are initiating or expanding a personal or family garden, or one with and for your community, it can be helpful to do some focused envisioning alone or with others so that your garden is aligned with needs that you are addressing and makes good use of human and natural resources available. Below is a template (to expand and then write into) to help you (or a group) consider your garden goals and vision.

1. What is a need in your life or community that you hope to address by growing food?

2. What are your big and small goals and dreams for your garden?

3. What is something you definitely want to grow or produce? Something you'd like to but feel unsure about?

4. What are the qualities that you want to bring to life through a garden? What features might enhance these (altar, water, bench, etc.)?

5. Knowing the land or space that you will grow on, what techniques will you incorporate?

6. What local resources exist—materials such as cardboard, organic matter, mulch, recycled containers? What about human resources (neighbors or local organizations)?

For fun or reality, can you envision a micro-business related to food and gardens? Could be anything from making an herbal or food product to a garden-based childcare program!

## Awaken the Power: *Contemplative Practice*

### *Making Hope Banners*

This activity is inspired by Tibetan prayer flags that are strung at Buddhist temples and between rooftops and trees so that prayers of peace and happiness float on the wind. Traditionally, the Tibetan prayer flags represent the five elements, and the flags include the mantra Om Mani Padme Hum that is related to the bodhisattva of compassion, Avalokiteshvara.

This emphasis on compassion and positive vibration inspired us to do an activity inspired by prayer flags with our teen program. It is a good one for a small group to generate or re-affirm collective values and hopes.

Get some colorful cloth (in a few different colors), and cut into approximately one-foot squares. You can purchase outdoor-quality cloth, sometimes called pack cloth, or recycle scraps. Old t-shirts would also work. Depending on the context and group, generate some key values or hopes for your program. With permanent markers, fabric paint, or paint markers, each person chooses some words or images that arose from the conversation and decorates one of the pieces of fabric with these. It can also be nice to do this in pairs. Share these aloud with no filtering as to what is or is not possible. String on a long rope, using clothespins, pins, or stitching (if stitching, be sure to reserve room at the top of the fabric before decorating to fold over). Ideally these will be outdoors, but they can also be shared in a common space indoors.

Let these ideas blow on the breeze of your vision to keep your values at the core, energize your work, or inspire new ideas. It is nice to return to these values and hopes periodically to reflect on how intention and practice are aligning, or to recharge your efforts outward.

## *Ten Ways to Be (and Stay) Creative in Your Work*

- Identify values/qualities you appreciate; keep these listed and close.
- Don't let the mundane stuff consume or take emotional precedence over creative vision.
- Don't get over-consumed with technology and social media.
- Create an altar-like area in your workspace for inspiring quotes or pictures, or other things that keep you reminded of the big picture.
- Generate a totally out-of-the-box, wild idea first and then think about how it might work, even if it doesn't.
- Listen more completely—to staff, partners, colleagues, the universe.
- Share ideas with others who think similarly as well as differently than you.
- Don't be put off by the fears of others, or your own .
- Prioritize annual time to reflect on and check alignment among your mission, projects/programs, personal/staff passion, and community/societal needs.
- Re-nourish your vision with contemplative walks, or by attending inspiring events (related or complementary to your mission), alone or with colleagues.

# Chapter Five

# Re-love-ution: Creating Strong Communities

## *Is This a Crazy Idea? Giving Birth to the Festival that Stinks*

The sun had been up for several hours when I rolled out of bed. This in itself was uncharacteristic for me, let alone that I was completely hungover. The morning after the very first North Quabbin Garlic and Arts Festival I could barely utter three questions to Deb: "Are you mad at me? Did anyone get hurt? How did I get home?"

I had not had much to drink at all in the previous decade. I had had no sleep and not much to eat in the forty-eight hours prior. 'The morning after' of our very first year of the beloved and enduring "Festival that Stinks" was immortalized.

A year prior to that beer-hazed morning, five of us had met over a potluck meal with a concern and an idea. We were bummed out that many of the talented artists and hardworking farmers in our region had to leave town just to find a venue to sell their wares, especially since the five of us at this table were among the hardworking artists and farmers who did so. It was 1998 and the 'buy local' craze was in its infancy. It had not yet hit our town and likely never would in the way more affluent communities would benefit from the buzz. We were culturally and geographically isolated from the nearby five-college region where farmers markets were burgeoning with Saturday morning latte-sippers filling canvas bags with organic vegetables and beeswax candles. We needed something unique to lift the spirits of the locals while supporting quality food and art. There was beauty and skill to be found in our region. It deserved celebrating.

Boston-centric media portrayed the demoralizing statistics about the North Quabbin—our new home—as downtrodden and rife with social ills, yet it was apparent even from our short time living there how ripe a region it was, especially in regards to folks who knew how to work with their hands. One late summer day during our first season on the land in Orange, our neighbor Jim—a native of the region and phenomenal woodworker—stopped in. Chatting while I bagged up a gorgeous crop of our garlic, we found ourselves sharing a similar lament. Where would I sell our beautiful garlic without traveling and taking a wholesale price-cut? Where could Jim show his stunning work that combined fine woodworking with items salvaged from local factories?

This spontaneous conversation led to a creative and fateful potluck gathering of five: Jim and his wife Alyssa, Deb and I, and neighbor and potter Lydia Grey. After dinner and with ideas flowing, we each dug into our pockets to produce a twenty-dollar bill, creating a crumpled pile of 100 bucks on the center of the table. We met every month, always over shared food, to plan an event that would, according to our mission statement: "Unite North Quabbin people whose livelihoods are connected to the land and the arts, and to invite both local residents and those who do not live in the region to experience the richness of an area that is often overlooked." We called local artists and farmers and found a dozen who were game to participate as vendors. A few hundred postcards and sheer creative will brought us around to the first annual North Quabbin

Garlic and Arts Festival one year later, a compelling if not unusual combination. We were energized. A multi-season reality show with episodes we never could have imagined had begun.

A few months before the first festival in September of 1999, our team of five gathered at the end of a sweltering summer day on a field on the far end of our land at Seeds of Solidarity, collectively envisioning: "Maybe the art vendors can line this side, and the food truck will park here...We can put together a small stage using some spare two-by-fours... this center area should be good enough for the raw garlic-eating contest. We can park some cars here, but not many—how about we ask Mike about using that field down the road for overflow?"

The week before the festival a hurricane surged through the East Coast and dropped a lot of rain on our parade. This was to remain a theme, but we didn't know that then. We called in any available tractor within five miles, and a bunch of friends arrived to move gravel. Jim and I built a makeshift stone bridge across a trickle that, with the hurricane, had become a semi-raging stream separating the soon-to-be-festival field from the entry. We were running out of time before the big day and had no way of knowing what to expect for crowds. So began the sleepless nights as I packaged garlic or readied the field for whoever might arrive for this crazy idea of a festival.

Festival morning arrived. It was drizzling. Some say rain is a blessing. If so, we've been multiply blessed. By 9:00 A.M. the sun came out and the fog lifted slowly, befitting the dreamlike quality of the experience. A good-natured group of vendors began to arrive, hauling tables and crates on dollies down the muddy path. By 10:00 A.M., the curious started to show up. With absolutely no idea if twenty or hundreds of people would show, we had arranged to shuttle folks in from a local elementary school lot, transported by a long-haired, tattooed school bus driver named Tom. Years before Google Maps existed, folks followed the wooden garlic signs blazed with directional arrows that Jim and I had nailed to utility poles in the dark of night. We heard that some shuttle passengers were skeptical once they hit the country dirt road, but once on the bus they became entranced by the magical mystery tour as Tom pointed out landmarks and told stories of the flooding of the

Quabbin. By the time they arrived at our field ten minutes later, they were primed to go with the flow and onto the grassy field they descended, some adding a few bucks to a big plastic donation bottle positioned on a crate near the untended entry. The dirt path led to an open field edged with a modest but merry assortment of artists, farmers, and food including a cooler containing a trial tub of Bart's garlic ice cream that would evolve into an annual staple.

Local legend Morris Metcalf drove a horse-drawn hayride around and around the fields. Music was made on the rough-cut lumber and bamboo stage at the edge of the forest. A garlic and egg toss got everyone playing. It was festive and wild, and many hundreds of people showed up to make living history as part of the muddled and muddy mass of humanity that attended the First Annual North Quabbin Garlic and Arts Festival on a September Saturday.

By 5:00 P.M. that day, the crowds had thinned and it was down to the organizers and friends who had traveled from near and far to lend a hand with cleanup. Dan Young, a local and co-founder of the People's Pint, unloaded a keg. We made a fire and scraped together whatever food was left from Myron's garlic fare. Beers in hand, we all pushed his food truck out of the mud amid relieved laughter. The stories of the day began to flow along with the ale. Deb headed through the woods to the cottage with baby Levi and some visiting friends, while I stayed in the field with my buddy Earle who had come out from Ithaca. We stayed close to the keg with other neighbors and friends late into the night, sending many raucous belly laughs through the forest. Earle eventually walked me home and rubbed my back as I sat on a log in the forest and threw up; getting home with the help of a good friend being the answer to the third question the next morning. And as to questions one and two, Deb wasn't mad and nobody got hurt.

That next day, Jim counted up the bills stuffed in the big plastic five-gallon water container we'd put out for donations. He was lucid enough to throw it on the front seat of his truck before the evening party. Seven hundred bucks—we were ecstatic. There would be a festival again the following year, and, as time would have it, for many to come. A tradition of living and loving local, neighborhood revelry, and a cultural phenomenon was born.

The founding festival committee poses for a publicity shot.

When Jim and Ricky built the first stage of scrap lumber, they couldn't have imagined that in a few years time...

the event would attract 10,000 people, over 100 art, agriculture, and food vendors, and not one, but three stages for great performance.

## Real Folks, Resistance and Re-love-ution

The first time we drove through the town center of Orange after looking at the piece of land we knew would likely become Seeds of Solidarity, the stretch of boarded up buildings peppered with junky front lots
and liquor stores felt pretty depressing. It still does in many ways, but
now we know many of the smart, salt-of-the-earth people that live and
work among them. Ricky and I may have been more comfortable in
a culturally diverse, small, urban community more similar to our respective upbringings. On our quest for land and community, we had
considered city living and creating an East Coast version of the Integral
Urban House (Berkeley circa late 1970s), but we wanted ample space
to grow a lot of food and breathe. The place we landed and live does
not resemble a college town, back-to-the-land Vermont, or a hip urban
enclave (although we enjoy visiting all of these). We ended up in one of
the poorest, most isolated rural regions in Massachusetts because we
could afford the land and wanted to participate in meaningful ways in a
community with real needs and interesting possibilities.

The Depression-era Boston-based land grab that flooded the Swift
River Valley to create the Quabbin Reservoir and promised jobs elimi-
nated four agricultural towns and geographically isolated our region.
Four hundred billion gallons now fills what up until 1938 was a fertile
valley filled with homes, farms, community centers, and generations of
indigenous dwellers and their buried ancestors. The eminent domain
seizure of this valley caused the demise of an agricultural economy and
the increase of an industrial, mill-based one in its place, which created jobs until manufacturing started to trickle away, leaving economic
despair. Arriving some years beyond this era of working class, relative
prosperity, the images of abandonment that met our eyes were pretty
dismal. So much so that Orange was recently used as the set for a Ste-
phen King TV mini-series called Castle Rock, with film crews and 1980-
era facades taking over for a while and bringing a somewhat surreal mix
of horror and appeal to town.

When we first moved here, I went into the town hall where the
clerk said something like, "Oh, you're the people with the funny last

names!" I realized we were in a place where (a) we were not only new-comers but also 'ethnic' newcomers, and (b) people might say what they thought and felt without censoring their comments. I prefer that, though, to wondering what people are thinking and whispering after I walk out the door. We have sometimes felt and been treated as out-siders, which is to be expected. Our fellow townspeople voted in the majority for the forty-fifth president. But as far as we know, our names and politics have not been any cause for challenge as we carried out some out-of-the-box things over the years, the Garlic and Arts Festival being at the top of the list. We, in turn, have done our part to show up—for causes created by others, and by serving on local committees and boards. We have raised hundreds of thousands of dollars to initiate and implement programs for all ages from toddlers to teens to elders, as well as gardens to revitalize barren downtown spaces. In small towns, people know what is going on.

When we were first settling here and people asked, "where's Orange?" we'd remind them of the radio ads heard on The River, the alternative music radio voice of the Pioneer Valley. The simulated voice of Fernando from the 1970s show *Love Boat* was resurrected to tell listeners about The Bedroom Factory in Orange, Massachusetts, "the town that almost had a Pearl Jam concert." We would later meet and become friends with Noel and Zita, owners of The Bedroom Factory. They transformed a sprawling factory on the Millers River—Minute Tapioca before it became The Bedroom Factory—into the Orange Innovation Center, an incubator for small businesses, artists and creative entrepreneurs in the region. We created gardens at the Orange Innovation Center, the local community health center, and the library—all organized as community workshops so attendees could both learn and make something meaningful together.

For many years, Seeds of Solidarity organized a daylong Commu-nity Food Forum at this converted factory as well. It served as an annual winter gathering where local residents from all walks of life taught each other skills for resilience. Our recipe for a Food Forum goes something like this:

*Take one central gathering space. Fill with about sixty people who heard through local media, agencies and word of mouth. Add one friendly volunteer to welcome people who arrive, another to receive potluck lunches. Stir in an opening activity to relax and connect the group. Divide the group in four roughly equal portions (by their own choice) into break-out sessions led by community members prepared with a food, farming, energy, building, or organizing skill to share. Let ideas rise for about 1 hour. Mix everyone back together for a potluck lunch. Season the lunch break with a short film, DIY activity, or facilitated conversation. Re-divide the group for another round of (same or different) afternoon workshops. Bake until golden with a culminating activity that integrates the experiences of the day, and inspires next steps.*

If you are a bird, getting to the center of town from the Orange Innovation Center by way of the Millers River is beautiful. But by sidewalk, you pass many of the addresses that show up in the police blotter. After a few blocks you reach Hazel's community clothing place, where people can fill a bag with a warm jacket, old sneakers, plates, and a coffee maker for a few bucks. A Seventh-day Adventist, Hazel has been a vegetarian for fifty years, and knew what to do with kale well before 'Eat More Kale' shirts underwent their first printing. The Millers River boasts the finish line of the annual River Rat Race, inspiring great athleticism by some and weekend partying by others. The river is home to an impressive diversity of dragonfly species. We didn't know this when we spent the first night in a tent on our land, but dragonflies swarmed in this area and so we decided to incorporate their winged image, a symbol of transformation, into our Seeds of Solidarity logo.

Just north of the main intersection in our town, Quabbin Harvest food co-op is housed in an old bank building. It was started as a weekly farm share effort under a pop-up tent by four local women wanting to feed their own and other local families well, and in a town that did not have a market accessible without a car. Before opening in the volunteer-refurbished building, community members removed debris and a chain-link fence to transform the adjacent parking lot cracked with years of neglect into a functional one for the store. We added accessible and abundant Grow Food Everywhere raised beds at the lot entry, surrounded by a landscape to attract native species and pollinators, all created in partnership with Mount Grace Land Conservation Trust. There is a sign in this garden that reads: "This Garden is planted by the community, for the community to celebrate Quabbin Harvest, your community market. You are welcome to harvest something to taste, or enjoy in a meal."

I once received a call from a woman in a college town to the south, seeking advice about how we worked with our local municipality to create Grow Food Everywhere gardens. In her city, as a liberal college community with a long history of support for the arts, she wanted to plant fruit trees in public spaces and was feeling tangled in the bureaucracy of what she thought to be a relatively simple idea. The response

We create gardens throughout our community to increase availability of fresh food, to teach people to grow their own with low-cost materials and tools, and to beautify spaces in need of vitality.

she received from Shade Tree Commissions and her Department of Public Works resonated with what-ifs, such as: "What if the ripe fruit falls on the ground and makes a mess? What if someone gets stung by a bee from that fruit on the ground and has an allergic reaction and sues the town? And who will take care of the tree and prune it or pick up the branches that fall after a winter storm?"

Ricky thought it intriguing that someone from a so-called progressive community was calling us in Orange, so often perceived as a poor and downtrodden town, to ask how to make positive change. As goes the Bob Dylan line in "Like a Rolling Stone," "When you ain't got nothing, you got nothing to lose." We've found that to be somewhat true about our community—there are many truly community-rooted organizations and agencies as well as residents, and the level of collaboration is impressive. One such organization is the North Quabbin Community Coalition, a highly functional network that unites local groups around real needs and creates task forces to address them, with lasting successes. There can be so much oversight and overthinking in some communities that it can thwart creativity and risk-taking. We concur with the adage that "it is easier to ask for forgiveness than permission." It keeps things fun and edgy.

As it turned out, our own neighborhood on Chestnut Hill Road was already rich with eclectic, resilient folks when we got there. It is the kind of place where, if you are walking your dog down the road it will take you twice as long, because any number of neighbors will have something to ask or share. For many years, we tapped the maple trees of the Dodges and Forsters, many of whom were born and died in the same house. We relish potlucks and tool-sharing with those who got here a decade or so before we did, built their houses and created livelihoods as musicians, social workers, woodworkers, potters, writers, and farmers. Sometimes, a visitor arriving for one of our Seeds of Solidarity tours will ask if we thought about living in community, meaning an intentional community. We tell them that we do, and it is called a neighborhood. It is not perfect. And we realize, too, that we are very fortunate.

We have learned a lot about self-determination by living in the North Quabbin region. We've seen that even in an economically struggling, isolated community with no shortage of trauma, people manage to rebuild their best version of a community time and time again. We have a motto in our home, be it in regards to a lousy day, car breakdown, or bigger life happening: "In this family, we don't give up." Likely by no coincidence, we landed in a neighborhood and a community with this same motto.

## *My Pen Is*

The library book sale was just getting underway when the director called me over, a Saturday morning coffee in his hand. "Maybe it's just me," he said with a cautious smile as he nodded toward the handcrafted sign that Ricky and I had installed the previous evening, "but it looks like it says 'penis.'"

Walt the library director had suggested we use a quote from Judah Halevi, a twelfth-century poet and Spanish (Sephardic) Jew to adorn a bench affixed to garden beds we installed at our local library. Being the lone Sephardic family and among maybe three Jewish families in our entire town, I was particularly pleased with his choice. I'd carefully painted Halevi's words "My pen is my harp and my lyre; my library is my garden and my orchard." Not carefully enough, apparently.

The library garden was the last of twenty raised beds that we had created that season. We had put them in a couple of weeks before the book sale event that would also be the garden grand opening. These beds were to be a contemplative garden for adults, with a mix of vegetables and flowers. We would add a simple bench with a cedar post to display the quote, and screw the whole thing firmly to the garden beds so all could be enjoyed (and while unfortunate to have to think about it, not stolen). As with similar community projects we had done, we had decided to create the gardens in a collective, educational way at a workshop where anyone interested could come and help while simultaneously learning to build a raised bed and get some gardening questions answered, too.

The June day we'd planned for this garden-making event started out with rain comparable to a waterfall and didn't let up much. In preparation, we had done our usual haul of materials the evening before. We'd loaded the bed of our truck with the lumber to make two 4-by-8-foot beds, pre-stained by youth in our SOL program earlier that week. At Clearview Compost, the source of fertile soil that made all of our gardens in the community possible, we'd lugged, lifted, loaded, and unloaded twenty-four ten-gallon barrels of a local compost/loam mix into the truck bed—twice. It takes about 1.5 cubic yards of materials to fill a 4-by-8-foot garden bed with 16 inches of soil—hard to imagine, but true! The sight of a big diesel pickup backing onto the lot next to the library didn't arouse too much suspicion since our truck full of garden supplies moving around by dark—the only time we could fit in such deliveries given the fullness of our days—had become a familiar sight to local police officers.

The rain let up only a little before we were due to start the garden workshop. We tried to energize ourselves for the project ahead by enjoying some music, snacks, and poetry in the library before heading out into the deluge to build some gardens. Wisely, the library staff opted to enjoy the antics from the warmth and comfort of a second floor window as if in a theater balcony, as we began the performance of assembling the beds and emptying in bucket after bucket of rich compost. It is actually great to plant when it is raining—a nice, warm, sunny day, the likes of which we rarely have for our events can (says me, the queen of optimism) be a bit much on young plants. And so, the seeds and transplants we had brought got a great start. By the time we were ready to install the benches and signs a week later, the gardens were showing lots of green.

I have painted many signs with quotes from activists, poets and spiritual leaders to adorn our farm, as have an assortment of our interns along the way. Writing these out is a nice meditation, and I generally letter shorter quotes freehand, with just some pencils lines as a guide. I use my fingers to get a sense of how much space is needed for the words to fall right, and it usually works out pretty well. At work on the Halevi quote, in my effort to ensure it would all fit, I may have squeezed the first few words in a bit close so it would all fit. This was confirmed when thirteen-year-old Levi walked in from school, threw his backpack on the couch, took one look at what I was doing and reported, "It says 'penis.'"

"My Pen is my harp..." he started to read.

"It does not," I replied defensively. He lifted his eyebrows and headed up the stairs, treading lightly on my artist sensibilities. I tried to stick a semicolon between 'pen' and 'is' to break them up. Levi came down for a snack.

"You can't do that," said my precocious, literary son. "You just changed the meaning of the poem. And it doesn't look any better anyway." Prior to Levi's direct assessment, Ricky had walked through the house and in his ever-agreeable manner offered, "Looks great," so I attributed the possibility of misinterpretation to my oversensitivity and my son's pubescent mind, and let the paint dry.

A few days later and just before the sign was to be installed at the library garden, some interesting visitors happened by our farm. Amidst conversation ranging from the techniques of Masanobu Fukuoka to politics in Central America, one of the visitors, a Brit working for an NGO in Central America, shared a seemingly random story about a billboard in Nicaragua that had attracted much attention by a sexually charged error in wording. When Ricky later shared this anecdote with me, he told me he couldn't figure out why the visitor had shared this particular story, until he realized that he had apparently seen the sign resting on a workbench, which triggered his memory. I was still not convinced that this anything more than the interpretation of a few high-testosterone readers.

The book sale morning arrived. We had managed to firmly affix the signs to the benches just in time. The mellow director had laughed it off. But then when a few white-haired trustees cupped their hands near my ear and giggled, "Do you think it looks like p...," that was it. I knew I could not spend the rest of the summer fielding remarks and snickers. Early the next morning, I headed over to the library gardens with sandpaper and a small can of matching paint and gave Pen  is the space it deserved.

## Guerilla Gardens and Pink Shoelaces

The windowsill next to our farmhouse kitchen table serves as an altar. Like all of the sills inside our home, Ricky made them to be wide and of smooth, colorful concrete. We bartered with our potter-neighbor-friend Lydia, who made us stunning clay tiles depicting hands and harvest that we affixed in the arched space above this kitchen window. When someone brings a gift of homemade jam, sends a special card or note, or if we come across a quote that suits the season or times, we place it on this altar for a while. For a time, there was a ragged pink shoelace there. I had come across it one November day while untangling ties from to-mato stakes along a sidewalk that had fruited well and fed many. We had planted the tomatoes along with towering sunflowers on the edge of an empty lot in the center of our town, and the pink shoelace held a story of this guerilla garden.

Guerilla gardening is a term used to describe growing plants on public or vacant land—a quietly political act to beautify spaces, provide nourishment, and, at times, reclaim land. The first year we created this particular guerilla garden, we didn't get to it until the Fourth of July, but that was actually a perfect date for the young people who chose to join this 'Interdependence Day' action. We originally envisioned the idea of a guerilla garden at a winter meeting of our SOL Garden youth leaders. Everyone became animated as we schemed about going to an abandoned lot in the middle of Orange under the cover of dusk and pre-tending we were picking up trash while actually poking random holes for sunflower seeds. But as the time approached, we figured we should do well by the plants. We would be bolder rather than clandestine. The plan evolved: we would line the edge of the land directly adjacent to the sidewalk with sunflowers and tomatoes in holes filled with compost and mulch them well, so that they'd require minimal maintenance and perhaps even thrive.

An old foundry had once operated at the far end of the lot, back when town was abundant with mills and meaningful work. Now only a large "Available" sign stood on this large eyesore of a lot, overpriced by the absentee landlords and depressing to all who passed.

We didn't ask anyone if it was okay, knowing this would trigger a domino effect of small town bureaucracy. We would meet late after-noon on the Fourth. The post office across the street from the vacant lot would be closed for the holiday and traffic would be minimal. Anyway, our massive old Ford pickup is a little hard to miss with its diesel rum-ble and tall wooden side slats slathered with phrases like "Seeds of Soli-darity Prana-Grown Produce," "Stop the Pipeline," and "Don't Miss the Festival that Stinks." Youth leaders Cody and Darnell sat in the back of the truck perched on a pile of shovels, along with two 55-gallon drums of water, twenty buckets of finished compost, and six flats of tall tomato and sunflower seedlings.

At our appointed meeting time, a few other kids arrived by bike and foot along with our co-program leader Jac and her husband Mark. We began our escapade by picking up the trash from the strip of land between the sidewalk and the lot. "You really didn't ask for permission?" asked Cody. I had only asked a friend who sat on the planning board how much land adjacent to the sidewalk he thought belonged to the town, rather than the lot owners. To add to the thrill of adventure  but also curious what might actually transpire, I half-jokingly replied: "If the cops come by, I'll take the rap. You just keep digging."

We'd been in this small town long enough and knew enough police by face and name. We paid our taxes; had started a festival; given innumerable hours to schools, local youth and families; and worked hard to develop positive relationships. We'd worked hard to do right by the town. Still, we didn't want the kids to get in trouble, and we wanted them to see how to do nonviolent action right. It was edgy but relatively safe—perfect for teenagers. Start digging, kids, we said. They did.

Once the trash was extracted and bagged from the grass on the overgrown lot edge, we marked out a line of thirty holes (two and a half feet apart) along the cracked sidewalk. Ricky pounded the hole-digger into the dirt. Cody followed with a shovel to scoop out as much of the rocky earth as possible. Darnell added a few hefty shovelfuls of the compost/loam mix to each hole. Cait laid burlap coffee bags around each hole to keep the weeds down, then covered those with some mulch hay. Mark and Jac planted the assortment of cherry and large tomatoes—we hoped this variety would please the little ones going by in strollers with their young cigarette-smoking parents, as well as the crew of post office workers across the way. Levi and Emily hammered in the stakes to support the plants, pre-adorned with small handwritten, laminated signs: "Planted by neighbors who care," "Help yourself to a tomato when ripe," "Good Food for the People!" and "You are my Sunshine."

We then placed a telltale "Grow Food Everywhere" sign in a central spot. As we scooped water bucket by bucket out of the drums in the back of the truck, Gary, the owner of the junk and antiques storage building on the other corner walked over to show us where we could hook up a hose, anytime. As we planted, we got the thumbs up from a bunch of cars, several positive horn toots and a holler out of a truck window, the passenger calling out "Thanks, that lot's been looking like shit for too long!" We took a photo of the big sign in the center of the lot that now formed the backdrop for this guerilla garden. Above the bold blue letters spelling out "Available" on the sign, we held our handmade paper ones: "Fresh Food... Available."

Over the summer months, the plants thrived. The sunflowers grew tall and bright, and were enjoyed by both people and birds. More than once I saw folks pausing to enjoy a tomato, and once saw some postal workers run over on break to check the ripening of some they had apparently been watching.

Good food is a basic human right. Sadly, 'healthy' often becomes synonymous with 'inaccessible' and 'expensive' due to packaged and transported 'natural' food products and corporate organic grocery chains deserving of nicknames like 'Whole Paycheck.' While the rise in farmers' markets, food co-ops, CSAs, and mobile markets is fantastic, fresh healthy food often remains far from the tables of those who need it most. The plethora of fast food chains and dollar stores in poor communities are among the perpetrators of malnutrition and disease. Simultaneously, generational knowledge and skills for preparing and cooking nourishing and culturally appropriate food has often been disrupted by factors that can be traced to inequity throughout society. The health impact is catastrophic, as evidenced by skyrocketing rates of diabetes and other diet-related diseases. Some use the term 'food deserts' to describe the absence of healthy food in many communities, but the term 'food apartheid' rings home the fact that racism and class inequity run deep within the food system. (Plus, deserts are actually very rich, ecological places!) While urban communities of color are disproportionately targeted by food apartheid, poor rural areas like ours also suffer from lack of access to affordable fresh food and to land.

There are many ways to increase access to fresh food for all. These include farm-to-cafeteria efforts that bring fresh local food to schools and institutions, and programs that increase SNAP (federal Supplemental Nutrition Assistance Program) benefits for use at local farmers markets or CSA shares at local farms. Pay-what-you-can cafes that double as training programs for those homeless or formerly incarcerated also offer compelling approaches.

As farmers and educators, our niche and passion is to teach people of all ages skills they can use to grow food in a variety of settings. Gardens spread throughout a community and for community members help decentralize food production and defy corporate control, build skills for self-reliance and resilience, beautify desolate spaces, and create living ecosystems. In many cases, they unite residents across age and culture. Guerilla gardens are one of many ways to Grow Food Everywhere and promote food sovereignty.

Even though we never planned on changing this planting from a guerilla garden to a more formalized arrangement, we wanted it to look good at the end of that first season especially. We intended to let it be a quiet success that we could continue to maintain without hassle or permission. On a late fall day, I walked along the sidewalk and stopped at each of the thirty plants that had survived and given all summer without any vandalism or uprooting. I went plant by plant, pulling and shaking precious soil from the roots of each back into its hole, removing the beige twine or cloth that held it to the stake, and tossing the plant towards the center of the lot (hoping some seeds might even sprout on their own the next year). I then stacked the stakes into my car to store for the following year. My rhythm was unbroken until I noticed a pink shoelace holding a tomato vine to a stake. I paused, wondering where it came from, as I knew it did not come from our efforts. It struck me that someone had come by and offered what they had to add some mid-summer support to a tomato plant. This scraggly cord of faded pink suddenly became a sweet symbol of care and community ownership.

## *Food for the Old Folks*

"I don't want any of that stinky stuff," growled the man emerging from his beat-up blue Pontiac as he examined the contents of his bag: heavy with ripe tomatoes and bunches of chard and kale spilling out of the top. He extracted a glowing bunch of prime-season basil revered by urban foodies and handed it back, mumbling thanks while pushing his car door open with his cane. Of the many local seniors who received a free bag of fresh organic produce each week through a senior farm share program (grant-funded through a regional agriculture organization) in which we participated as farmers, he was one of only a few that grumbled at the plethora of greens and lack of sweet corn. Most were a consistent delight and ever-grateful for the fresh food on their limited income, which for most was just a monthly social security payment.

Each Thursday throughout the summer months, twenty senior citizens would arrive in a crumbling parking lot shared by the Senior Center, Ocean State Job Lot, and a Chinese takeout restaurant. Polly was one of the recipients as well as the volunteer who journeyed to our farm to pick up the weekly bags. Waiting elders easily located her car once its trunk opened to reveal bags overflowing with kale, tomatoes, and squash. The vegetables had been harvested from their plot and our farm fields that same morning by youth in our SOL Garden program. Garden carts loaded with the bounty, the teens pulled them to the top of our driveway amid laughter and satisfaction of a good morning's work and deed. They would wait for Polly, a senior herself, to transport them to the other elders. In a small community like ours, it turned out some of the kids were feeding their own great-grandparents or neighbors.

During the seven years we provided elders with food through this program administered by CISA (Community Involved in Sustaining Agriculture), we added some special events that would make the youth/senior citizen connection even stronger. In the early years, SOL youth and staff organized a harvest meal for participating elders, which enabled kids to do one of their favorite activities—cook—while celebrating and sharing their harvest. Using churches or schools to serve the meal, about forty seniors would attend and enjoy local roasted chicken along with our tomato and bean salads, freshly ground cornbread, pesto pasta, and peach-blueberry crisp. In turn, the youth would hear stories of gardens past, or recipes and canning still enjoyed. We did this for a few years, but found that the midsummer heat sometimes caused too many seniors to cancel at the last minute. When the Quabbin Harvest food co-op opened, it made sense to pass on the administration of the program, as well as some of our farm produce (for a modest return) to them rather than organize the distribution. This was one of our aha moments in which we realized we don't need to do everything.

Over the years, some of our efforts were sustained and grew. Others were right for a few years, and then transitioned into another program, or into the hands of another entity. Senior FarmShare served to deconstruct perceived barriers as young people debunked myths of being media-consumed and lazy, and senior citizens had the opportunity to share their wisdom and stories of the land with these teens.

## Peace, Love, and Garlic: The Sequel

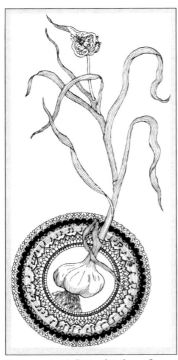

Our son Levi drew this logo for the eighteenth annual festival.

Someone clangs the big wrought iron bell hanging off of the family stage a few times. A few members of the afternoon festival setup crew are already mingling around the tables near the wood-fired bread oven, where the end-of-the-day spread is looking good. There are kebabs from a festival food vendor born in Afghanistan. There are some tasty looking sandwiches from Terry, who makes and sells an array of horseradish products, a giant quinoa salad for the vegans made by a local weaver, and a Crock-Pot of farm-raised meatballs ogled by the carnivores. The big bell is clanged again to call in those still immersed in tasks like laying out the fencing in the parking area, raking wood chips to help level the entry path to the Spoken Word area nestled in the forest, or pounding in the last stake of the kid's activity tent. Someone drops a stack of signs indicating chef demos, free water stations, or musician parking that they'll resume placing around the field after our festival workday lunch feast.

The North Quabbin Garlic and Arts Festival has become a great success, attracting 10,000 people over a weekend and requiring about 150 volunteers plus parking teams, engaging over 100 exhibitors, along with thousands of person-hours to organize, set up, and take down the festival. It has become much more than we ever could have imagined when five neighbors got together for that potluck meal. The festival has become a force for cultural and economic vitality, a favorite destination for families near and far, and a generator of many wild and joyful stories.

Deb's extended family are among the regulars, offering endless support in many ways.

But about twelve years into the festival, the committee, which had grown over the years to a core group of about fifteen, was starting to burn out big-time. We held a day retreat and decided we wanted to carry on with this event that was loved by many and that offered a powerful message of community resilience. The organizing group needed to make some changes for our sanity and sustainability. We discussed hiring one person to be the administrator, but that felt messy as others on the committee would still be doing comparable work for free—and how would we value some tasks more than others? We really couldn't be sure there would be enough profit to create a paid position while keeping admission low and accessible for local families—and while refraining from sponsorship, which was also an important element to all.

At our stand, our dear friend Phyllis knows how to sell garlic.

Being that we were all well into midlife if not further, a big piece of the

burnout was the intensive physicality required to get the whole shebang
set up: raising and securing huge tents, pounding fence poles, setting
up our handmade wooden picnic tables in the food cafes, putting up
gobs of field and road signs, rolling barrels into place for multiple recy-
cling/composting stations, designing and laying out three large parking
fields, and the list went on. We decided to build in a model of exhibitor
participation. It was one of the best things we ever did, and now we
don't know how we managed without it! All art, food, agriculture, healing arts, and community organization exhibitors were asked to sign up
for four hours of work as a required part of participation in the festival.

Still a critical part of the festival, exhibitor work time collectively
provides hundreds of essential hours. Some choose to sign on for one
of six workdays in the month leading up to the big weekend; others prepare food for these crews, or choose from assorted other tasks. It was
initially cumbersome to organize 120 people into tasks, but an online
tool called SignUpGenius has since made this fluid. We do still have
some vendors who don't use the computer, so we match them up to
needs directly. Participation in this way is not for everyone, which is
fine as we now have plenty of interest from returning and new exhibitors with the festival's popularity. We encourage vendors to think carefully about this component before even applying. Community building is one of our core festival values, and this unique element makes
it much more than a 'show up and sell' event. Interestingly, we have
observed that since implementing the exhibitor participation element,
vendors rarely rush in and out or complain about their location; they are
now a part of making it all come together and feel the sense of ownership that this brings. By staying the path of volunteerism, the festival
has been able to give $5,000 in grants each year to local community
causes that propagate the arts, food, wellness, energy, and community
building themes of the festival.

On a typical Sunday preceding the festival (one of six workdays),
about twenty people are sitting in a circle at Forster's Farm, the festival
site, enjoying lunch after a productive afternoon of site work and setup.
A shady spot near what was the milk house is our typical gathering spot.
Neighbor, craftsman and baker Doug built a bread oven off of the milk

house shed that runs all festival weekend to provide a special snack to volunteers, and the slate prep area when not in use for bread making serves as a great buffet counter. Festival committee member Steve has taken on the task of coming up with a question for whatever group has assembled on a given workday. Some are quick but revealing—like your year of high school graduation, or your favorite movie—while others— a time you have been arrested, your favorite place on earth, or story of your first kiss—can keep the circle rapt, listening and laughing for an hour. By the end of a typical festival workday, everyone has contributed meaningful and essential labor, broken bread together, shared stories, and made fruitful connections.

While the pieces of bringing the festival to fruition are not visible to attendees, the trash-free emphasis is. Many understandably pause with disbelief when they learn that we create only three bags of trash for 10,000 people. A U.S. household can make three bags of trash in a week, or maybe twice that after a Christmas week of holy plastic tossing—so how can 10,000 people (most of whom would not self-identify as environmentalists) keep their collective crap to only three bags over a weekend of festive food, fun, and celebration?

Going for no trash was an easy discussion for the festival committee from day one as a down-to-earth group already steeped in do-it-yourself values. From early on, food vendors wanted to participate, which meant we could define the parameters of their participation to prohibit polystyrene as well as help them source compostable serveware. Compostable products are much more available than when we started (though this adds another challenge in learning which are truly compostable!) We prohibit the sale of bottled water and provide water for free. In order to educate the public as well as sort waste correctly, it really helps if waste stations are staffed at all times by volunteers to help guide the festival folk to dispose of their stuff to the correct stream— recyclable or compostable. This requires a large team of volunteers— in our case, over twenty-four people, each working a half-day—plus compost captains who circulate, educate, and help the other volunteers change out full bags. The main challenge to a trash-free event is controlling what comes in from the outside world. It is important to us not to alienate the locals that head over to the festival after a morning errand or football game, but the Dunkin' Donuts iced mocha latte in an extra large plastic cup with lid and straw that they arrive still sipping doesn't have an easy place to land at the festival, nor do the granola bar wrappers that parents pack to keep their little one content. These, food vendor gloves, and diapers are what generally make up those three bags of trash.

We've evolved the design of our stations over the years. A plywood cover sits over eight 55-gallon drums, with holes cut in the plywood directly over each drum. This cover is brightly color coded and clearly labeled as to what goes where, and a median partition provides an eye-level display with sample

It takes a committed crew of volunteers to result in only three bags of trash for 10,000 people.

items and where they go. To further celebrate and educate, we have a 'Gardens not Garbage' display that includes large, clear jars that show the process of festival compostables becoming finished fertile compost—enough for twenty four-by-eight-foot garden beds! In order to think full-circle, we invite people to 'vote with compost' by putting a small scoop of it in the bucket of their choice to indicate where they would like to see gardens in their communities, with options like a food pantry, childcare garden, post office, jail, school, and elder housing.

Creativity keeps our group and the festival thriving, and this unfolds in the planning process as well as in the three stages of performers, or among the sixty workshops and playful garlic games the weekend of the event. We meet monthly year-round over a potluck; these meetings include the occasional heated conversation, but much more laughter. We started the festival to create a venue for local farmers and artists as well as unite those within and outside the region. We have never done a business plan or a needs assessment, the results of which would have most likely come back doubtful that anyone would show up on a field in the middle of one of the poorest towns in the Commonwealth. In addition to being an important economic and cultural engine as well as super fun, there are so many connections that happen at the festival, and we will only ever know about some.

There was an article in our local newspaper that started like this: "A few years ago at the North Quabbin Garlic and Arts Festival, two men got to talking about making farms more viable and cutting the region's energy use." Remember dairy farmer George Hunt who asked about our solar panels at Seeds of Solidarity Farm while delivering a load of composted manure? Having gotten some answers to that question then and more answers yet in the 'Portal to the Future' renewable energy area at the Festival, the sun now shines on enough panels sited on the Hunt family's rocky, non-tillable land to power 1,500 homes. Others may have sold out to a big-box store for a big wad of cash. The Hunts had that opportunity. Instead, their choices resonate with "Orange is the New Green," one of our favorite festival slogans along with "Peace, Love, and Garlic" and the original "The Festival that Stinks."

For two days each year, the festival emanates and celebrates the qualities of a world that we—and perhaps many others—want to live in. It has affirmed for hundreds of thousands of people—not the least of whom are the friends and neighbors who co-create it—that such a world might be possible.

## Seeds of Change: Apprentices and Interns

The Festival that Stinks is perhaps our greatest contribution to community revitalization and the re-love-ution. That said, mentoring over forty young farmers and educators has been an integral part of the fabric of our Seeds of Solidarity years. We are heartened by the passion, purpose, and spirit they demonstrated. We are humbled by the love and leadership they continue to manifest in their lives and communities.

Just as the workings of our family farm are distinct from the programs of our nonprofit wing, our farm apprenticeships are distinct from our education center internships, each with its own parameters and learning goals. Ricky mentors those on the farm; Deb mentors those interested in youth and community education. Farm apprentices have lived on-site for extended periods of time, whereas interns come once or twice a week, often as part of their college study or other

Interns and apprentices share in a sweet, quiet moment on the farm.

requirements. Several exemplary interns have transitioned to education program staff. In addition, there has been a stream of assorted and wonderful volunteers, many who stayed around long enough to become part of our lives—just as every apprentice and intern has in some way.

As soon as we were able to transition our family to our finished larger home, we began our farm apprenticeship program, and then continued it for a decade. We brought on two people at a time for a six-month period. For the first few years we sought a couple, as their accommodation was the cozy one-room little house. Rowen and Gordon were among the early apprentices. Rowen had already begun her path as a seedswoman while a student at Hampshire College, as informed by her Haudenosaunee lineage. She and Gordon, a wonderful musician, now raise their beautiful family in Northern California where Rowen carries forward the traditions and wisdom of indigenous people as a seedkeeper, and is a sought-after educator.

While we had a few more years of wonderful couples, we realized that we could house farm apprentices in individual cabin tents and use the little house as common space, enabling us to host two single people. We later even built what we call the treetop loft over a farm outbuilding, a lovely pine-floored space with private sleeping areas. Apprenticeship days were filled with morning meetings followed by whatever farm or building task of the day Ricky had planned. The energy and laughter emanating from the fields added great energy to the Seeds of Solidarity, and friendships were made among apprentices and with our family that

Farm apprentices got to know each other quickly, living and working. together all day...

...sharing stories in the fields...

...and with no shortage of wild produce delivery rides.

would endure. While we prepared a weekly Tuesday evening feast at our table followed by check-in time, the little house continued to serve as common space for apprentices to cook, play music, read, hang out with visitors and the like. We can still readily picture Max and Jason making breakfast, Megan and Caroline creating art, Mark and Rebecca planning their next life steps together. 'The Jamie's'—one a male poet and Jeopardy aficionado, the other a female athlete on her way to become a social worker—made for a great apprenticeship year (if not some confusion with communication). These apprentices' role in the life of our own son was significant; he was raised with a seasonal extended family of cool twentysomethings in addition to his own crazy parents. Many became and remain fabulous farmers, while others had their passion for building, art, or human services fueled while at our farm.

As Ricky began to incorporate more meditation into his own life in pursuit of balance and sanity, this too became part of the apprenticeship search. We sought those who wanted to work with the land, and who were also on a spiritual path in some way. The apprentices that we attracted in later days enjoyed an optional morning meditation, and the sounds that emanated from the fields and greenhouses included recordings of teachers from a variety of traditions and walks of life (to which the apprentices contributed), and rich conversation among the crew. When we ended the apprentice program after many great years, we were simply seeking more sacred space on the land for our relationship and family, given that we were involved with so many people in other realms of our education programs, community engagement, and the festival.

We decided to list shorter-term experiences through WWOOF (Worldwide Workers on Organic Farms) for the times we most needed help: spring planting and late summer garlic harvest. We got a host of replies that did not stand out, but a couple that did. When I saw Angelo's email, it was so unique that I called Ricky in out of the field to read it. Indeed, this warm and kind Toronto-born actor/poet would end up returning for four summers and remain a beautiful part of our extended family and lives. Heather was another beloved volunteer-turned-intern-turned-summer-land-dweller who treated our sacred little house with great respect, and carried her compassionate ways forward to become a caregiver and doula.

Meanwhile, we also had interns (who lived off-site) and added yet more energy to our lives, and to Seeds of Solidarity as a whole. When we began, very few colleges had farm and food system tracks, so students interested in these fields created their own majors, often seeking hands-on experience or credit through their institutions. We've had many interns from Antioch New England Graduate School (where I had previously taught), UMass, Amherst College, and Greenfield Community College. Some worked in our school-based and afterschool gardening programs; others helped with community work, such as our Grow Food

Many apprentices and interns became and remain like family, à la 'Bruncle' Angelo (brother to us, uncle to Levi).

Everywhere for Health and Justice Program. There was always an intern helping to develop curriculum for, and co-teach our SOL Garden youth program. Along the way, some carried out terrific program evaluations, as well as helped to create many materials that enabled us to share our program successes and how-to ideas nationally and internationally. We have had interns sow Seeds of Solidarity and their own excellent work nationally and internationally, often returning to their home communities to do so. Caitlin was among the early UMass sustainable agriculture students and an early intern who initiated an innovative farm on the North Shore. Sta was called to a second career, reclaiming gardening skills while recalling the wisdom of her grandmothers in preparation to return to her country of Zimbabwe to develop economic and food security programs for women. Being good mentors was and remains very important to us, and we spent a great deal of time meeting, co-working with, and supporting many amazing young people, knowing they would carry the teachings outward in meaningful ways. Our own mentors had been critical to our evolution, and we were committed to paying it forward.

Some experiences can click right away, others take a while to digest and integrate. Cain, a recent intern who also worked on our farm and with our SOL youth program, carried out interviews with three former farm apprentices and three former education interns to learn about what their experience meant to them, and how they continue to sow seeds of change and solidarity.

Jen was our first ever intern. In 1998 she was a UMass student

Our connection remains deep with our first intern, Jen.

shaping her own concentration in sustainable agriculture before it was a recognized major; we still have the drawing Jen did of our first greenhouse. Jen and her husband Pete have two beautiful children and run Woven Roots Farm in the Berkshires where they practice no-till methods. Jen, a Colombian and Jewish woman, describes a special, early moment in the field with Ricky:

We were opening up the soil and seeing this incredible micro cosm before us and the conver sation that we were having was linking me and him to all of our elders before us, all of our leaders... those who [worked the land] because they had no choice, and those who were moved to, and what their community beckoned them to do... but we were making an active choice and building on all of the efforts of ancestors before us.

Jen was not sure her path would lead to being a farmer or marrying her then-boyfriend Pete. Her words about commitment and relationships are a great honor for us to hear:

The work that I did there opened me from the bottom of my heart [and] enabled me to believe in something deep within me that I had never allowed to shine; it enabled me to see that doing this work was something I really deeply wanted to and was meant to do in partnership with someone else. I am fascinated by Deb and Ricky's rapport with one another, their admiration for and deep respect for one another. It came at a time when my parents had just recently split up after being together for twenty-six years and a lot of what dismantled their relationship had to do with them not being able to follow their hearts...[Deb and Ricky] introduced the possibility that you can follow your own convictions and you can seek what's right for you as an individual while elevating somebody else, being in partnership with somebody else—and that symbiosis is something that we witness everyday all around us in nature...I am able to have that be a source of joy for my relationship with my partner.

While not all parents of interns and apprentices appreciated that their recent college graduates were potentially pursuing a livelihood not known for grand paychecks, most parents came to appreciate the work ethic as well as the happiness that exuded from their children. We felt an instant connection with Jen's father.

I chose to introduce my dad to Seeds of Solidarity and to Deb and Ricky, and at a point when he was having a hard time... it was a tremendous turning point in his belief in me, and what my potential was, and he started to realize that what I wanted to do maybe wasn't so crazy, and he started to really appreciate the innovation behind it... and [he carried that] really for the rest of his life... He passed away suddenly, a few years ago... Something happened in that field that was a transformation... and I'll never forget that. I could never thank them enough for that... It gave me tremendous peace of mind to be able to know that when he passed, he believed in me, and he trusted that my path was good.

Carrie and Catherine were both interns with our education programs and with some overlap. Carrie had farmed prior to working on a master's degree in geology with a focus on climate change and was in intern turned co-leader in our SOL Garden youth program; Catherine was a student from the South with a full ride to Amherst College

who re-invigorated her dormant environmental studies while there. Starting as a volunteer, Catherine came to co-lead our Grow Food Everywhere community programs, creating gardens for low-income families. Both speak to their dedication to uniting social justice and community organizing with environmentalism, and how their work with Seeds of Solidarity supported and informed this fusion that is not often the norm.

Says Carrie: "Deb and Ricky made the choice to buy land that nobody wanted, and picked a community that many people continue to turn their backs on...the rural experience of poverty is not as appealing to most people [as working in urban communities]. They taught me how to find the social circumstances that are uncomfortable and walk towards them rather than walk away from them." Carrie continues to carry a social justice analysis of the environmental and food movements forward and into the organizations within which she works:

> Deb and Ricky helped me think about the cultural appropriations associated with agriculture—sometimes found in permaculture for example. They have been able to recognize and honor the sources of knowledge that came before them. I'd never experienced that in agriculture before. The land conservation movement is an incredibly heteronormative place [...] I've been noticing in my [current] work that while the white land conservation movement drops back

to [early] Native American experience, there is a skipping over of the African American experience of the land, and slavery.

Carrie speaks to the balance of self, relationship, and action that has been integral to our own lives, and therefore to our mentoring. "[They show] incredible respect for themselves, relationship, family, and community... I've become a more demanding person in work relationships in the nonprofit world where there is generally a sense that you will give so much of yourself—it is very tricky when you then need to advocate for yourself for work/life balance...I'm still working on it every single day." Carrie articulates a core theme that has universal impact: "Loving, authentic relationships is what they try to teach at SOL Garden and through all their work...that is what Deb and Ricky do, they model this."

While Catherine was at Amherst College, she was aware that they had existing programs for students to connect with local organizations, but they tended to focus on urban centers and work with youth of color. "As a white woman," she reflects, "I was looking for a place that tackled the same types of issues—but I didn't want to be another white person contributing to having a 'savior role' in a communities of color."

Catherine worked with our Grow Food Everywhere programs, putting in gardens for low-income families (as was her own family in Georgia). She describes being able to combine her college-aged idealism with real challenges, and learning to navigate that balance. She began thinking that the families were "Going to grow all this food and it is all going to be rosy. At the same time they are doing that, it is also very challenging—we worked with a lot of families that had a lot of issues going on, so to continue to engage with families in the good times and a lot of difficult times—not idealistic in the way that you would dream of, but it didn't mean those undertakings aren't worth it and really valuable."

Fluent in Spanish and Portuguese, Catherine came to us after spending time in Brazil where she worked with a land reform movement. After graduating, she pursued an interest in nutrient reclamation and peecycling, which took her to Chiapas, Mexico where she met and later married an indigenous man engaged in similar work. Currently a regional planner in Vermont as well as a board member with the Rich Earth Institute—a leader in nutrient reclamation from urine—she and Flavio also reinvigorated a community garden in their community, where Catherine referred back to a lesson learned from her internship at Seeds of Solidarity.

> "My motivation was fairly pragmatic—literally Grow Food Everywhere to save the world. So [while we were putting in a garden of both flowers and vegetables at a community health center], I asked Deb how you make the decision to use this land for flowers as well as growing food. She gave me a look and replied that cultivating beauty was just as nourishing and feeds us just as much as food does—and if you were to only grow food and not cultivate beauty, art, home-making, space-making, community building—what is the point if you don't have a holistic, human experience happening at the same time?"

Fast forward to their community garden organizing, where Catherine and Flavio sought to engage neighbors who had previously experienced the garden as overgrown and untended. She hoped to give them a harvest basket, but the produce was not yet ready. "It dawned on me that we had all these huge sunflowers so I went and I cut them a huge bunch of sunflowers—they really appreciated it and I told them they could go and pick sunflowers any time. That was a full circle moment. I was so focused on the food—the purpose—and sometimes it is, and sometimes it is to create a beautiful community space."

Catherine sees a chronic perception among planners and in communities in need of support and revitalization: expectation that an external force—such as an outside company—will save the community, moving in and providing jobs. "It is very clear to me that it is not about waiting for that external force—it is about identifying and nurturing the strengths within the community." She describes her time at Seeds of Solidarity and her work that followed as "affirming that social transformation is possible—but you need to look at the long game, not what you are getting this week. [I've learned that] every drop in the bucket fills the bucket and it's worth it."

While some people may have a sense of their passion and path early on, others have a pivotal event or just realize that the life they are living is not aligned with their values and purpose. Jon left what he describes as "a very conventional life," to apprentice on our farm, leaving his Midwest town and engineering job. Jon was also pursuing a meditation practice, and was among the early interns who sought this as well as immersion into local food and other skill-building. While at Seeds of Solidarity, he gained building skills that enabled him to work in this way, as well as build his own tiny house, and to continue, along with the woman he married, to prioritize meditation and contemplative practice within his life.

Jason is a charismatic people person and a deep seeker. He responded to our apprenticeship call with a desire to experience a summer immersed in farming. But, as was the case with so many of our apprentice/intern relationships, we'd come to find that our lives were meant to intersect for various reasons. He describes walking down the farm driveway and having "that feeling I belong here." Jason and Max were the apprentice team that year. Both ended up gathering years of experience on other farms after leaving Seeds of Solidarity, remaining with farming as passion and profession, and sustaining a solid friendship forged while they were here.

While Jason does currently use tractors and equipment in his position managing a nearby campus farm, he notes that farming at Seeds of Solidarity made him hyperaware and he does practice reduced tillage methods. He also took with him what he reflects on as "ideological way of living that is sustainable to the people and the planet—so basic, yet so profound."

Jason carried skills, leadership, positive presence (and a t-shirt) to many a farm after Seeds of Solidarity.

Farm apprentices and interns alike have all spent hours at our farm table from the initial tea and interview to lunch breaks to dinner gatherings. Kaitlin, then a graduate student in environmental education, shared the importance of this informal bonding during her internship: "There was something really sacred about that time; soup, bread, and salad from the farm... They have this amazing ability to attract thoughtful, interesting people—there was no shortage of people to talk with over soup—their really rich network of interesting and talented people. And at the start of each meal we would take the time to show gratitude—something that I continue with my family." I was blessed to perform the wedding ceremony for Kaitlin and Chris, who used to work in an organ tuning and building shop across from Seeds of Solidarity. As others have mentioned, we are honored that our relationship offered a positive model of communication: "Deb and Ricky have strong communication with each other—core strengths that enabled them to make the space to allow their passions to evolve and their work to take on innovative directions."

Kaitlin and Chris continued back to Toronto, and eventually to New York's Hudson Valley after her internship morphed into several years as staff in our SOL Garden and school garden programs. "I definitely learned a lot from Deb just about her bearing in workshops, curriculum design, her ability to listen intently to questions, and allowing the space for students to come up with good questions... and that all has a higher purpose rather than just a lesson."

Kaitlin (left, with UMass intern Susie) came as an Antioch environmental education grad student and continued to work with our farm-to-school programs for many years.

As a small organization, it is our hope and intention that our practices ripple out, and we encourage this through our programs, publications interns, and all who visit. Says Kaitlin, "A large number of people have had the good fortune to come in contact with Seeds of Solidarity. Everyone leaves with some nugget of inspiration—however big or small—that they take home. I think that has a profound impact."

Jen, our first intern speaking two decades later echoes this sentiment. "I think their impact is bigger and brighter than any words can ever probably put to it... Inspiration is something they are able to share on a daily basis, weekly, monthly—to hundreds and hundreds of other people... Deb and Ricky have the capacity to share their love and knowledge in a way that is so tangible to people—they don't ever isolate anyone or make it feel like it is not accessible...they've done a phenomenal job of drawing people in, and collaborating with more people so their impact can be greater. There is no doubt in my mind that the work they are doing has had a global impact—both in practical skill and an energetic awareness."

## *Some Days, Other Days*

"It must be great to work outside all day."
"This must take a lot of work—you must be tired."
"You are really living the simple life!"

We've heard all of these and more over the years, and all hold varying degrees of truth, depending on the day! It is hard to grasp—let alone bring balance to—a self-created life. Each day is indeed different. Juggling a farm, a nonprofit, the needs of a relationship, friends, family and household, and engagement in other community endeavors and social activism is a constant work in progress. There is a great deal of freedom embedded in our life and livelihood, yet at the same time, no one else is writing the paychecks and there are bills to pay. There are challenges to create balance and boundaries within it all.

### *Some days look like this:*

I wake up planning to get in a full workday of envisioning and designing a new program, starting with a little yoga, just like I'd put in my calendar. I make breakfast for our son Levi before he gets on the school bus, while also searching for his soccer jersey for a game that afternoon. I pour my tea, put yesterday's clean dishes away, shower, and I waver—do some Sun Salutations or a quick email check? I make a bad choice and check email but resist the temptation to reply to anyone, and do what I should have done first: turn off the computer, reheat my tea, and roll out my mat for a few quick stretches. But my mind is already a bit away from my original intention. *Gotta do it differently tomorrow.*

I head to my home desk. Oops, I realize it is the sixteenth of the month and the monthly department of revenue and federal tax filings are due...yesterday. People don't always think of this stuff when they dream of how great it will be to start a nonprofit—I didn't! Okay, computations and filings done. Now, time to get creative and envision that new education program.

I hear a knock on the door downstairs. I pretend to not hear it. The door opens. "Hello? Anybody here?" A neighbor has a question. I say a quick hello. Most people don't understand what I do, and being able to work from home much of the time has its ups and downs. The farm is the most visible, so many neglect to realize that my life is often an administrative stream of events.

I realize I never ate breakfast. I am hungry and my mind is starting to wander, so I make a bite to eat. It is now 11:00 already and I feel I've gotten nothing done in the ways I was hoping to. Another email has come in: a grant rejection. I need to take a walk. I go outside, walk, and feel better. Now I feel nervous about funds for the coming year, and instead of creative envisioning, I switch to slight panic. I make some tea and drink it while it is hot. I decide to refocus my day to do whatever I possibly can to restore my original plan. I add a few things to my list for the next day: pick up compost for the childcare center gardens, thank the volunteers on the Garlic and Arts Festival recycle crew, send out another reminder about our upcoming farm tour, drop off the crates of spinach ordered by our local food co-op on my way to the bank. I remind my weary self that it is all good, that this is my choice, and that the little things shall pass. I manage to get myself in a pretty good space, and get in a solid hour of an intended four of creative program development. Sometimes it all feels like too much, but then there are other days.

### *Other days look like this:*

We get up early as usual and everyone is in a good space; Levi goes off excited about a poetry contest at school and Ricky shares a sweet conversation shared with his friend and farmer Pete while he drops off a truckload of compost. They have brought a gift of a chicken pot pie that will be our dinner one night soon, and they left with a big bag of salad greens that will be part of theirs. Contemplating the day, I sit quietly for a moment and look out at the land that we are so blessed to come to know and feel safe upon. I sip my tea and scratch the dog's head as he relaxes.

I roll out my mat and do a little yoga while Ricky goes off to meditate. He comes back and we have breakfast—he picked a few raspberries from the greenhouse that we enjoy with some yogurt and maple syrup that we tapped and boiled with our good friends Dan and Julia. We check in briefly about plans for our SOL Garden youth program, as we have a session later that day.

We enjoy breakfast together, aware that one of us could be on Route 495 headed for a day job we truly dislike without food to nourish our family. We each do our own thing in the morning. Ricky waters the greenhouses and checks on the garlic fields. I organize materials for a course we teach to men incarcerated at the county jail, plus confirm some upcoming visits to our youth program from a local chef and a poet. Our SOL Garden intern and the other youth program staff arrive. We catch up on each other's lives for a few minutes, reflect a bit on the previous week, then gather some tools and things we'll need for the afternoon session. The spring day has warmed and the sun feels sweet as the van pulls up after having stopped at two area high schools, and the teens in our program amble out.

We sit in the circle, passing bags of popcorn and cookies. Everyone shares one word that describes how they feel in that moment. It is good just to listen, and to know that the opening circle, no matter the question or conversation, is a way to center before we launch into topics, guest visitors, gardening, and building projects as part of this food justice and resilience program that has been core to our educational initiatives since the inception of Seeds of Solidarity. Putting out energy is always a bit tiring, but feels so good after. They leave. I harvest some of the nettles along the path to SOL Garden where there is a huge patch.

I head down to the house, stopping to grab the mail. No bills, nice. And one surprise, a modest donation from someone who heard a presentation we gave a few weeks back—how heartwarming as well as needed. I steam the nettles, cook some potatoes with garlic greens from the field, and blend them into a quick and tasty soup. I mix up a batter for cornbread while making a few calls to check in with friends. Our family sits to eat. Ricky reads a beautiful piece of writing that he came across and wants to share. We enjoy the food from our land. We are tired from another long day, but mostly grateful as it has been one that makes us remember why we do what we do.

A good day from the early days: gathering sap and heading to boil it into syrup at Roundhouse Farm with our dear friends Dan and Julia.

*Field Guide Chapter Five*
*Rebuilding Community: Love Over Fear*

## Questions to Ponder: Self-Determination and Revitalization

- What do you know about the natural and cultural history of the place you live? What do you have yet to learn?

- Who are the people and organizations in your community (or field) that you consider leaders? What qualities make them so? Who are some movers and shakers beyond your community—currently and historically—that you respect, and why?

- What does justice mean to you? How do you experience injustice in your life or community? How do you experience and/or perpetuate privilege?

- How do you (or could you) contribute to a stronger, more positive, and more inclusive community? What needs in your community do you have the passion or skills to respond to? What are actions that have or could ripple out more broadly

as models for others, potentially with national or global impact?

- Have you faced resistance in efforts to build community or
carry out creative projects where you live or elsewhere? What
did you do, what could you do differently, or what systemic
issues created barriers?

- What does a truly resilient community look like to you? Consider spiritual as well as physical resilience. How close or far
are you (individually and as a community) from that vision?
What is a next step towards this vision?

## Down to Earth: *Do it Yourself*

### *How to Throw a Trash-Free Party for 10 to 10,000*

A major effort at economic and cultural revitalization in our community
has been the North Quabbin Garlic and Arts Festival that we co-create
with our neighbors. And of all of the sustainability elements of the festival, three bags of trash for 10,000 people is a compelling ratio that
prompts many to ask how we do it.

For a small gathering, it is a bit easier to do. Some of the same
principles apply: use as many compostable products as you can—and if

a small party, washable (let everyone help!). Have an easy and fun way for guests to sort food waste and recyclables from trash, as well as a way to deal with it after the fact, like a home compost pile or farm or facility that accepts compostables. Consider a set of compostable utensils along with simple paper (or tree-free) tableware as a wonderful holiday gift for friends or family to then have on hand for gatherings. A larger supply could be a meaningful gift for such organizations (like food banks or religious institutions) that put on weekly or holiday community meals for those hungry. Unfortunately, these organizations often use 'cheap' polystyrene. With multiple products on the market, Biodegradable Products Institute (bpiworld.net) is a good and frequently updated source to verify whether certain brands are in fact compostable, and to learn more about the range of products and suppliers available.

When it comes to larger events such as festivals, it is important to bring the conversation and related values into your planning from the get-go, or well in advance of your event if you are making a transition to recycling and composting. Here are some tips!

**Transition to trash-free.** If your event does not yet even recycle, start with recycling, and then add on a composting program in the subsequent year. You can also start by having vendors go polystyrene-free, adding the requirement to use compostable utensils the following year. It is easier to have a trash-free festival as a core event value from the start, but if you are transitioning, consider doing it in stages. Keep vendors informed about the trash phase-out plan so they feel engaged. Humor always helps, too!

**Clearly and enthusiastically explain your policy** in any initial application materials that are sent to food (and other) vendors. For example, this is excerpted from the North Quabbin Garlic and Arts Festival application for food vendors:

> *Our Festival Trash Free Policy: Once again, we only produced 3 bags of trash last year, with 120 bags of compostable material transformed into garden soil! This would not be possible without the support of our amazing food vendors. Thank you! Consider the no-trash policy very carefully before applying. No Styrofoam/polystyrene or plastic plates/cups or wrapped-up plastic stuff. Paper plates and cups, preferably white and un-*

*coated, are great as they can be easily composted. Aluminum foil is okay as it can be recycled. Plan and order well in advance. The organizers are happy to run through your menu with you, and help you brainstorm products or serving ideas.*

**Enlist committed volunteers** to oversee receptacles or stations, and to educate. No matter how informative your signs, human presence will increase effective sorting and reduce contamination. Provide them with gloves and a tool to retrieve things placed in the wrong receptacle. Reducing contamination is critical if your compost is going to a commercial farm or composting facility and you want to sustain this relationship. College environmental groups can be great to enlist as volunteers. Keep volunteer shifts reasonable, and honor your volunteers with a meal, t-shirt, entry pass, or special thank-you note. Some events have attendees put everything in one container, then volunteers sort everything off-site—but then much of the educational opportunity and sense of waste diversion ownership is lost, plus it is a little gross.

**Pre-arrange with a farm, municipality, or composting company** to pick up and/or receive those bags of glorious compost. Do the math. It may cost you less to pay them for their service than pay for trash disposal. It is true that some costs—such as compostable bags—will be higher than plastic. It may be helpful to seek a small grant or business sponsorship to cover such costs. They will likely still need to do a little sorting for 'trash' contaminants, but hopefully not much!

**Create fun, bold receptacles** for compost and recyclables, or if you have the funds, order them from commercial suppliers or check with your local or state recycling or solid waste district, as some provide loaners to community events. Simple signage, and smaller holes that fit the types of items to be disposed of will help participants pause before dumping. Be aware of the weight of the containers to ease set-up and emptying.

**Make entry and field signs** celebrating successes, such as how much attendees and vendors have helped save from landfills and how much compost for gardens has been made.

**Encourage healthy competition** through trash-free games or prizes at the event.

## Awaken the Power: *Contemplative Practice*

### *Draw your Sphere of Influence*

The concept of a 'sphere of influence' is sometimes used in international relations or commerce to describe an area within which a nation or business wields dominant power. Alternately, the sphere of influence is also a powerful model to consider the ways in which an individual or couple can work to transform oppressive practices and systems. Building on this concept, try this practice:

On a piece of paper, draw a small circle, and then three concentric rings around it. Think about a social, environmental, or health issue that is important to you. Write it in the center. Label the next circle outward, 'Individual/Family,' the next 'Community/Region,' and the largest 'State, Nation, or Globe.' In regards to this issue and looking at the concentric rings, where do you feel your sphere of influence is at this time? In any or all of these concentric rings, jot down some ways in which you currently enact your values or take action. Contemplate this for a moment. Also consider where you feel challenged or uncomfortable. Where is your edge? What are some meaningful personal goals moving forward?

The intention of this exercise is not to judge yourself or others, but to recognize that we all have a sphere of influence in regards to some issue and in some capacity, rather than letting fear, silence, or complacency rule. Individually and collectively, people can work to enact positive power and change in a multitude of ways.

If you wish, repeat this practice with another issue of importance to you, or try the exercise with someone else to share your experiences.

### *Ten Ways to Do Small Acts of Good*

- Strengthen community in your own neighborhood: hold potlucks, barter/share skills and tools, share healing support, and gather to share stories and dialogue.

- Serve on a board or volunteer with at least one local grassroots or municipal organization.

- Train in doing work such as restorative justice, non-violent communication, or being an active bystander.

- Be a better communicator and listener (we all can). In group conversations, step up if you tend to be silent, step back if you tend to take up a lot of space.

- Make and share art, food, and creativity. Amplify this energy over excess technology.

- Celebrate the charitable energy of others; show up and support the causes and events that others initiate.

- Be an ally to others different from you, be it in terms of race, ability, sexual orientation or class. Be open to how you might be useful, not based on what you think others need. If you are in a position of privilege (e.g. male, white, cisgender, heterosexual, able-bodied), be attentive to power dynamics so as not to further perpetuate injustice.

- Dedicate time or spiritual practice towards a person in need of healing or support.

- Be attentive to your boundaries and overextending; practice self-care to avoid burnout.

- Keep ego in the backseat. Know you can't "change the world." You can influence—but not control—outcomes.

*Chapter Six*

# A Love Story in Progress: Marriage and Parenting

## *Our Big, Jewish, Buddhist, African Wedding*

Walking from the Leverett Peace Pagoda to our friend Micky's to get dressed for our wedding was going to take a while, so I put out my thumb. Someone I vaguely knew picked me up and asked where I was headed on that early Saturday morning in September of 1994. "To get dressed for my wedding," I replied, which caused him to take me a bit out of his way and right to the house, where my mother and special women friends would meet to primp and fill me with love.

It was to be a big wedding of about 200 guests. We'd been preparing for months; to-do lists covered the walls of our bedroom in my parent's retirement house in Montague (which we were renting and helping to upgrade). We had not yet found or even looked for the land in

Orange that would become Seeds of Solidarity. Our knowing that it was the time to commit and marry had come the year before, soon after reuniting after seven years of separate lives and places. This decision coincided with another that reflected our shared dedication to nonviolence.

Ricky had closed up his life as a farmer in Ithaca, selling the land for a pittance to get away from his farming partner. Upon arriving in Western Mass and moving in, he was working as a builder for money plus volunteering at the Peace Pagoda, where he learned of the vision for the Interfaith Pilgrimage for Peace and Life. We were lying in the grass near our garden. He stood, plucked a calendula flower, and returned to my side. He asked me to marry him and to join him on the pilgrimage. I said yes.

We planned a special weekend to bring our parents together in order to involve them in the wedding preparations and to share with them our reason for going on the pilgrimage. It did not go well. My parents, though lifelong lefty activists, were terrified that we were joining a cult and might follow them blindly into extreme danger. Ricky's much more conservative parents would have preferred a traditional wedding, but were surprisingly open—perhaps as he was the last kid. And, their first child to marry—Ricky's brother Bob—had broken them in years prior with a Sikh wedding at the ashram where he lived for a decade. With our plan to get our extended family's unconditional support having failed, we simply proceeded with what we needed and wanted to do to create our special day.

The ceremony was to be held at the Peace Pagoda, and the party would be on the front field of my parent's home in Montague. We printed invitations at our local copy shop on tree-free kenaf paper with a quote from Lao Tzu's *Tao Te Ching*: "In dwelling, live close to the ground. In thinking, keep to the simple. In conflict, be fair and generous. In governing, don't try to control. In work, do what you enjoy. In family life, be completely present."

As the date approached, we crossed off items on the lists tacked to our bedroom wall: lettuce and sunflowers in the garden planted to coincide with wedding harvest, tent and tables ordered, vows written, and a hundred more details. We met with our friend Phyllis Brown to contemplate the social justice and environmental values that she would weave in as our ceremonialist. We found some readings and symbolic items representing our Jewish identity to honor our ancestors. We asked Brother Kato and Sister Clare for a short blessing, which doesn't really exist in the Nipponzan Myohoji Buddhist tradition—so we got a long blessing. And of course, being farmers, food was big. We gathered friends to help us harvest and make roasted garlic and fresh tomato/mozzarella appetizers and several huge grain, bean, and greens salads. Chicken and veggies were grilled on-site. The cake and tables were decorated with our garden's multicolored sunflowers.

Once the final preparations were finished the Friday evening before the big day, we snuck off. We had thought we might go sleep at the Peace Pagoda as we planned to wake up early for prayers on the day of our wedding, and so had given our bedroom to visiting friends. Instead we decided to sleep on the ground under the big tent where the reception would take place. I don't think it was comfortable, but it was definitely memorable to dream on the earth in the space that would soon hold hundreds of dancing and feasting family and friends. We woke early and slipped out to the Pagoda to meditate with the drums and chant. Then we each went our separate ways, agreeing to meet at the Peace Pagoda dojo about half an hour before the ceremony.

I returned from my morning of pampering and getting dressed— someone must have insisted on giving me a ride so I wouldn't need to hitchhike back—and found Ricky in our appointed meeting spot. He was dripping but it was not raining out. "Are you sweating or did you just shower?"

"A little of both," he stammered.

We hid in the woods and watched from behind the trees as our beloved community hiked up the rutted road to the top of the hill and to the benches that we had built for the occasion, thoughtfully arranged by our best man and best woman, Earle and Kim.

Later, I would hear Ricky's story of the morning and how he almost missed our wedding. He had wandered into the forest near the pagoda to do some pull-ups from a tree branch to calm himself and gotten lost. The grey dome of the sky that day looked a lot like the Pagoda stupa, an off-white hemisphere. The overcast sky and his nervousness caused him to lose his way in the forest. He had ending up far off on the main road just as people had begun to arrive, so he'd run secretively back up and through the woods. Almost missing our wedding had kept him sweating even after a quick shower. I'm glad I didn't know this until much later.

Our friend Francesco had positioned his giant gong on a narrow land bridge in the middle of the lovely Japanese water garden adjacent to the Pagoda. A large flat area beyond the water garden had been the site of the first temple that had burned down. The monks and nuns offered it as the area upon which our guests could sit and face us as we made our way towards them to stand with Phyllis, Earle, and Kim on great flat stones at the edge of the water. Our signal to emerge from the woods and to this spot was the third gong. I had moved into a pleasant state of out-of-body-ness, only brought partway down to earth when I heard Ricky say, "That was the third gong, here we go."

We walked hand in hand out of the forest. I continued to feel pleasantly ethereal as Ricky led me to face the pagoda with palms together, across the rock bridge to greet our parents with hugs before finding our place on a large stone where the ceremony was to begin. The faces in the crowd appeared as one collective body of loving support. My dress was handmade of simple, off-white rayon. A silk scarf of rose, violet, and brown had been incorporated into its arms and waistband, fabrics chosen with a group of my women friends earlier that summer. Ricky had traded in his standard Carhartt overalls for a black cotton jacket and white shirt from one of the early fair-trade clothing companies. It felt lovely to stand on that rock with a little breeze, with some showers teasing but not arriving until the ceremony ended—and then, very gently.

The ceremony was beautiful, if maybe a little too long for some. There were a lot of parts to fit into our big Jewish, Buddhist, African wedding. We had composed vows, and penned letters to each other that we had not previously shared. We had written our own ceremony to be read by others. So, though we actually hadn't fully realized this beforehand, we were able to be silent, just feeling the day and the love from those there to witness and celebrate.

When it was over, Ricky and Earle loaded the chairs into trucks to bring back to the reception tent. I once again found myself without a ride from Pagoda to the party a few miles away, which I gratefully accepted from my friend Susan.

The afternoon and many hours into the evening were filled with all that we had hoped. Food and drink flowed, and ample rock and roll and Jewish dancing filled the tent, fields, and gardens, punctuated by the traditional chair dance. At one point the need for more salad necessitated kicking off my heels and dashing into our adjacent garden for a quick harvest, perhaps foretelling the many a bowl of our farm-fresh salad we would fill for countless celebrations in the years to come.

We partied into the night; even as the crowd started to thin, night brought a few more people invited for the laid-back, reggae band that turned up the bass and eked out the last energy of those gathered to party. While we danced, unbeknownst to us, friends had decorated the teepee on the edge of the field, filling it with candles and flowers that we collapsed into when all was done, too tired and full of love to make more. On each anniversary since, we read and recommit to the vows we wrote. They offer relationship re-centering, and guide choices such as the time early on in our home building when we put down our own hammers to travel to South Carolina to help rebuild a Black church, one of 145 torched during a racist crime wave in the mid-1990s. Not knowing when we married what was to come in our lives or the world in which we live, our vows remain current and guide our union and our work together.

### Our Marriage Vows

*We commit to:*

*Support and challenge each other, to work through the hard times, and to be each other's best friends*

*Continue to grow stronger as individuals and together, and pursue our dreams*

*Honesty, to listening and to understanding*

*Togetherness and to space*

*Keep our minds and spirits open to change*

*Take risks in our relationship and for our beliefs*

*Spiritual growth*

*Remember that from the earth we have come and to the earth we will return*

*Work towards peace and ecological balance with conviction, integrity and compassion*

*Conscious education of ourselves and others*

*Work towards equality and justice, and to learn from the histories and herstories of wisdom and struggle*

*Not sell out our values for material gain*

*Live our lives together lovingly, simply, humbly, and creatively.*

## *Learning to be a Dad: Protecting my Son from War and Rain*

As I think back on learning to be a dad, tears well in my eyes. My love for our son, my relationship with my own father, and the fatherless young men we've had in our youth program merge and swell the emotion. There is a lot to this task of showing up as a present father in this day and age.

Our first pregnancy was semi-planned. We were getting ready, but weren't quite ready, having just moved onto the land and with almost nothing in place that resembled a nest. Our friend Reed and I were working together in the field when we heard Deb wailing with pain upon discovery of our miscarriage. It was this pain that woke me up to fatherhood. I had not truly realized what having a child meant until seeing my partner with so much grief over this loss, after three months of planning and coming up with names. Our miscarriage instilled the sacredness of having a child. Three months later we conceived Levi, and on July 5, 1999, he was born. That was quite a powerful year for Deb and me: Levi was born, we started SOL Garden, and it was the inaugural year of the Garlic and Arts Festival. We were both thirty-six years old,

in the prime of our life, and with a lot of energy to release to the world. We planned to have a homebirth, but after sixty hours of labor we went to the hospital. Levi was born in health and peace, with our midwives and dear friend Kim right by our side.

I spent that first night with our newborn swaddled in my arms while he got his feet printed and all the other new baby things that happen in the hospital. I returned home the next morning to check on the farm. On our message machine was Deb's acceptance to be interviewed for the national fellowship that would be our primary income. Here we were, the second year on our land, living in our 12-by-24-foot studio without running water, and just starting our teen program. We were building soil on marginal land as quickly as we could, growing crops for restaurants and ourselves and garlic for the festival. Our first ever Garlic and Arts Festival was to happen one week after our return from D.C.

For several days while Deb was in meetings, I was Mr. Mom. Was I up to the task? Only time would tell. Deb pumped milk in the morning, and we tied together hotel towels to make a baby hammock. On day two, I decided to take Levi out of the hotel for a little journey. I packed him in our little snuggly carrier with miscellaneous supplies. We still were not quite used to all of the things a twelve-pound creature might require, such as multiple changes of clothes over a few hours' time.

With our pilgrimage including time in Vietnam still fresh in my mind, along with having several veterans as friends, I wanted to visit the Vietnam Veterans Memorial. It was incredibly powerful to experience the wall. I laid my son on the earth in wrapped blankets as I photographed him in front of all the names reflected in the background. I thought about the many mothers and fathers who lost their sons. As a new father, the power of the wall took me deep. Levi and I continued on to visit the Korean War Veterans and World War II Memorials. I thought of my father and his wartime in the Philippines. I knew in my heart I would do whatever necessary to keep my son out of a war.

Then the rains began. Tears were running down my cheeks, so it took a bit of time to realize the hurricane had landed and, yes, we were outside in the middle of it. My new fatherly instincts kicked in, and I ran to a nearby athletic field while holding Levi close to my chest. I sought cover under the roof of the bleachers. I opened the backpack as torrential rain came down and changed his diaper on the bleachers. A family of Japanese tourists, also seeking shelter, came to my rescue to help me change a squirming newborn in less than ideal conditions. I bundled Levi up into what I had that was still dry, and we hastily made our way to Deb's meeting location for our appointed time so she could nurse him. Thankfully it was fairly warm out. We arrived soaked but ready for feeding time, with Levi naked and loosely wrapped inside a cozy blanket, bouncing and happy. I knew then that I would do whatever I could to protect and love him.

## Pages Missing from the Parenting Manual

As we waited outside the principal's office, I wondered: have we ever needed to meet with a principal about Levi before? I couldn't remember. I remembered casually talking to his elementary school principal, who thoughtfully observed that, although he was an only child, he was not isolated given the flow of interesting people through our lives.

When he was a newborn and through his toddler years, we didn't have much choice about who was sleeping where. We lived in one room. By the time he was nineteen months I was ready to get him off the boob and sleep through the night, and more than ready to get out of a one-room dwelling, especially during the dark days of winter. The sense of expansiveness when we moved into our larger house where he had his own room was a gift. This was about the time we would think about having a second child. We were closing in on forty. Each month we'd say, "What about this month?" But we were never quite ready, and we were feeling pretty content with the satisfaction of moving into our house, reclaiming our relationship, and settling into some fluid times offered by the nonprofit and farm becoming more established. A few more months went by before we asked ourselves, "what if we didn't?" We had moved to a rural, predominantly white, mostly working class and poor community. This meant that the public schools, with funding inequitably based on property taxes, were under-resourced. We were philosophically committed to public education and unimpressed by the regional charter school. We were not advocates of charter schools for a number of reasons related to equity and their negative impact on rural school districts. We knew homeschooling would not be a good match for him socially—nor for us—so we all did our best to make schooling succeed. Levi likes structure, and he was able to thrive and excel with some teachers and programs, athletics, and through his own determination while maintaining his individuality.

He carved his path through adolescence as we did our best to keep him loved, alive—and with our humor intact. There was the time that he got a text from his first girlfriend that she thought she was pregnant. I will not likely forget that this happened in the middle of his cousin's rehearsal dinner the night before a big family wedding. Or that he knew he could immediately turn to us and ask to go outside and talk, while we tried to remain centered upon hearing that not only was he having sex, but also that we might be grandparents. As it turned out, her text was an immature joke revealed quickly, but one that kept Levi, Ricky, and me up half of the night in a cathartic mix of tears, incredulous laughter, and deep talk.

We remember clearly the moment he ran into the house breath-less one April day after track practice when his car had hit a rock. He hadn't just hit a rock: the car was perched three feet in the air balanced precariously on top of a huge boulder. A month into his license, he learned the hard way that you cannot take the curve in our dirt road at 35 miles per hour, especially when the road has just been graded. We affirmed that we were deeply grateful he was in one piece. And once we'd rejoiced in that, we added that he'd be paying for the repairs. When we confer on life with our dear friend and Levi's godmother, Kim (as we have often throughout our thirty-year friendship), she jokes about "another page missing from life's instruction manual." Parenting is a particularly amazing work in progress with no script, but for the most part, it's a beautiful ride.

The reason that we finally did go to talk to his principal was be-cause he was penalized by the National Honor Society for choosing to go to a compelling, in-school debate carried out by his peers rather than watch a Spanish-language television show in year four of a sadly useless language program. He was so charged up that he spent a solid hour researching and writing a letter explaining his actions, along with serv-ing an office detention. When a punitive letter came home from the NHS advisor assigning twenty hours of community service in the most restrictive and uncreative manner possible, we decided it was time for a meeting with the school principal. The great juxtaposition is that this letter arrived the same week as his acceptance to college which named creative thinking and intellectual curiosity as celebrated criteria. The principal was a bit surprised, I think, as we didn't come in with accusa-tions or excuses. Levi was there to resign from an organization whose values were not aligned with his own. As we listened to their thoughtful conversation, proud of his maturity and communication skills, I con-sidered messages we hoped to convey as parents: act with integrity, "be impeccable with your word" (a reverent nod to Don Miguel's teachings in *The Four Agreements*), be kind, respectful, and loving. One of Levi's mentors, a Creek elder named Cayoni, encapsulated it clearly with his words when our son went off to college: "Walk a straight line."

Levi is a fabulous art-
ist, gifted writer and orator,
and really a fun person to
be around. An entrepre-
neur, at nine he sold greet-
ing cards featuring his
photos, then for a few years
raised and sold pumpkins.
From there, he developed
a more serious business,
producing t-shirts featuring hand-drawn mandala
and sacred geometry art.
After doing really well two years in a row at the Garlic and Arts Festival, he continued to sell them out of the back of his car at school. He
strengthened his work ethic working at a restaurant during high school,
and by initiating his own landscaping jobs to save money for college.
Once when he was younger, we asked a well-respected channel if there
was anything else we should be paying attention to in regards to his life
and being the best parents we could to him. "He chose you and this life,"
she said. "He's alright; just keep working on your own stuff."

People ask if Levi is going into farming, or another environmental field. Um, we call him "Imelda Marcos" for his expansive shoe collection that would not really mesh well with farming muck. So, he won't likely take over the farm, and that is truly okay. At the same time, now that he is in college we hear and see the ways in which a strong work ethic, caring extended family, and values cultivated in a neighborhood rich with talent and eclectic characters has informed his ways of being and his worldview.

One night midway through his senior year of high school we were all up late together. He was reading poems aloud, seeking one to choose for an upcoming recitation contest. It was a cozy winter night and I recall feeling especially content, proud, and grateful. We didn't get an instruction manual with this parenting gig, but so many emotions are inscribed invisibly on this land where Levi gestated and experienced a vibrant childhood that carried him to adulthood. Our 'instructions' have been sun-warmed, muddied, and snowed on. They remain a work in progress. He is unique and beautiful, and makes life so meaningful— and parenting together is an amazing part of the journey.

## *"Tomato Atonement"*

*An essay written by our son Levi Baruch for his application to college.*

My face was still tear-streaked the next morning. I crawled through the jungle of green, sunlight warming the orbs that hung from leafy vines above me. The greenhouse was a different world, thriving with life. There are five greenhouses on my family's farm. This one had tomatoes, and I needed tomatoes.

I was here to repent. Two tubs needed to be loaded beyond full with my harvest.

Growing to thirteen is a big deal for Jews. Extended family asked what I would do for my Bar Mitzvah. Meanwhile at school, few were even aware of my religion. As the lone Jewish kid among 800 students, I was occasionally asked why my skin was slightly darker than everyone else. I would respond that my Sephardic ancestors came from Turkey, Spain, and Portugal. Those roots were important, but I knew I didn't want to spend hours in a synagogue memorizing Torah—yet I *was* transitioning into adulthood and needed to address that shift.

My non-traditional rite of passage would include teachings from important male mentors, arranged with my dad.

We first went to Apollo's house. An elder known for bounding up mountains, I knew he would test my athleticism. Soon we were in a parking lot beneath Mt. Monadnock. Mid-hike, Apollo jumped off-trail. Suddenly we were sprinting through brush and climbing cliff faces. When we finally summited, I collapsed and mentally willed my heart not to explode. Apollo proceeded to balance on his head. After maybe eight seconds, he leapt up and said it was time to go. People dove off the path as we careened down. Somehow, I made it back alive.

My next guide had a different task for me. Cayoni is a strong contender for the most badass man alive. A Creek Indian, he grew up in the Okefenokee Swamp and entered WWII at fifteen. He has a picture of himself at every battle in my history book. I was nervous, not because I'd recently seen death on top of a mountain, but because Cayoni caught rattlesnakes for fun. Luckily, our work was rattlesnake-free. I shaped a knife blank and sanded a hickory pole while he told me stories. I had a spear, made by my own hand.

Instead of a synagogue, my ceremony culminated on our farm. Those who had watched me grow offered me wisdom over food, laughter, and a roaring fire. Above the fire, resting on steel grates, a cauldron bubbled. My dad had spent the day harvesting, separating, and stirring tomatoes tirelessly. All his work was there. The heat made the grates droop, leaving the cauldron at a disconcerting angle. Everyone around agreed the sauce should move to higher ground. With two sticks I pushed against the cauldron.

*Then the worst happened.*

The vat got stuck. Or the grate shifted. Maybe undulating sauce disrupted the balance. Whatever it was, I watched the tomato sauce cascade. I saw gallons of hard work lost to the flames. My father strode over. The man who usually possessed a meditative disposition held rage in his eyes hotter than the flames between us. It was the angriest I'd ever seen him. Night wore on and I tried to remain appreciative through the gifts and hugs. In my head, my father's yelling reverberated. Later I snuck away and cried, angry and ashamed.

The next morning I went to the greenhouses. I filled the empty tubs, then carried each to the fire pit. I turned a sauce mill, like my father had the day before. I built a fire, then sat with the sauce as it thickened, stirring while the sun moved across the sky.

As the sun set, my dad said he was proud of me. My repentance was fulfilled. I had learned the importance of physical resilience, working with my hands, and growth from adversity. I had learned—

When life gives you tomatoes, make sauce.

## *Field Guide for Chapter Six:*
## *A Love Story in Progress: Marriage and Parenting*

## Questions to Ponder: Relationships and Commitment

- When and how do you create time and space for physical intimacy and other expressions of love with your partner? What are some techniques that work in your relationships (with partners, friends, and other family members) to deepen and express love?

- What factors create challenges to living your life from a place of love?

- How do you express intimacy in non-romantic relationships?

- How do or can you take risks in your relationships that result in growth and deeper love?

- If you are a parent or plan to be, how would you describe your approach to parenting? What parenting qualities have you observed that you appreciate? If you partner with another, how do/might you balance each other as parents?

- What else do you do personally or in your primary relationship to increase a state of love within? What do you do in your life to magnify love outward to others?

## Down to Earth: *Do It Yourself*

### *Magnify Your Love*

We utilize this exercise in a weekend workshop that we teach at the Omega Institute called "Magnify Your Love: Sharing a Life of Passion and Purpose." The process sparks powerful conversation, and can be done with your primary partner or a close friend, or with a few trusted couples. Create a quiet, comfortable space and allow at least an hour.

Individually and quietly, read over the relationship practices below, and consider one that resonates the most. Then, each person (be it a pair or a small group of three or four) takes a few minutes to share the one they chose, and why. If you are talking with a small group, it may be helpful to be with those who are not your life/romantic partners. Practice attentive listening. Have each person share without interruption for 4-5 minutes while the others simply listen. After each person has shared one theme, open the discussion. If more prompts are needed to continue and deepen the conversation, repeat, with each person sharing a second theme from the list, or take a few moments to generate additional practices that might be added to this list.

### *Relationship Practices* (Feel free to add to or personalize this list!)

**Uphold sacred boundaries** around the elements of your life and work. Hold meetings, especially around shared work so that work-related conversation does not invade the sanctity of relationship or family time.

**Embrace your differences and put them to work.** Know your differences and your respective strengths. There is benefit to working both together and separately. Identify your respective domains as part of your shared work.

**Be as loving and kind as you can** to yourself, your partner, and children—in work and while out in the world, in both small and large interactions.

Prioritize intimacy. Even with a lot going on in full lives, take the time to connect physically, intimately, and sexually. Nourish your relationship in some way each day, as well as with the gift of extended time, such as a retreat together.

**Be present in communication.** Listen deeply. Don't bring up old stuff when new things arise. If you start to go down a well-worn (poor) communication road and find yourselves pulling in old stuff, pause and ask, "What is really going on here?" in order to get to the heart of the underlying pattern or pain. Consider: what if nobody has to be right? Find your own techniques (gestures, code words) to lighten tension in the moment and to playfully remind you that these are but patterns. Trust that you can change, that your partner can change, and that patterns in your relationship can change.

**Learn when to accept and when to change.** Each of us has learned survival techniques over our lives. Learn what to accept of each other, and what and when to change for the benefit of the relationship and for individual evolution.

Create space within your togetherness. Your partner cannot meet every need and interest. Evolve, create and play together, but support your partner in friendships that help them evolve. Pursue and maintain both a shared spiritual practice and your own practice or teachers/mentors.

**Take risks for the things you believe in.** Stay awake to the suffering and injustice in the world and find your most authentic way(s) to participate in action and as an ally.

**Be open to or seek wisdom and guidance** from other realms: plants, your ancestors, healers, or spirit channels as they resonate with you. Consider that you can influence outcomes but you cannot control them.

Live your life as a ceremony. Seek to weave the connecting threads of values that foster harmony among your lifestyle, work, activism, spiritual practice, and relationships. Give pause for and enjoy the simple, daily rituals of life.

## Awaken the Power: *Contemplative Practice*

### *Create a Love Altar*

You may have an altar in your home for religious or spiritual honoring, but what about creating one to celebrate, energize, or help heal aspects of your relationship and love? Like most altars, it can be created with a few simple, sacred objects—heirloom, crafted, found, or bought for this purpose. Initiate the process together in a relaxed moment—perhaps on a Sunday afternoon, or a special occasion like Valentine's Day, the New Year, or your anniversary. Locate a spot that you see or pass often, such as your bedroom. You might start with a beautiful or significant cloth on a table or windowsill, or piece of wood on a few bricks. Take turns adding something that you have collected for this creation. Quotes, bits of poetry and phrases or affirmations that inspire you (or that relate to a personal or relationship pattern you are working to shift) are wonderful to add. Your altar could be a place you rest your wedding rings if/when you remove them, or where you add mementos from marriage, anniversary, a trip, or a special date. Make it beautiful, make it together, and make it reflect that which is important to you, or which you hope for.

Keep your altar fresh with flowers and scent. Always feel free to add to it or change it. If you are in a good place together, your altar is a sweet place to sit and meditate—if you are in a hard place together, its is a place to bring you back to what is important.

## Ten Ways to Increase Intimacy in your Relationship

- Be kind and complimentary most of the time.
- Dream of what you will do together, be it this weekend or long-term vision.
- Create time for yourselves that is free of talk of children, money, or life details.
- Keep candles on hand: they are lovely during meals or in the bedroom.
- Exercise together (gyms, walks, hikes, yoga, or whatever you like to do).
- Have at least one, shared creative pursuit or interest (such as music, dance, art-making, gardening, cooking, or reading poetry).
- Ask each other questions about emotional/spiritual wellbeing.
- Support each other's individuality, interests, and time with friends.
- Share your relationship challenges and joys together, and with trusted friends.
- Enjoy a lasting embrace each day, perhaps upon awakening or before sleep.

## Ten Ways to Be a Loving and Clear Parent

- Express love and have fun often.
- Start conversations with compliments.
- Say what you mean and mean what you say.
- Actively teach skills for independence and resilience.
- Don't take yourself too seriously; and don't take your children too seriously.

- Model good communication in your own relationships.

- Be honest (as is age-appropriate) about some of the things you are working on in your own life; it is not all about them, and self-reflection is good modeling.

- Stay aware of what is unhealthy, or dangerously available in their world (nobody is completely immune).

- Know that most things will pass, but take explorations with the big stuff seriously (sex and drugs) as these can result in things that do not pass.

- Support them with tools for their own health and wellness that they can carry forward in their own lives (from knowing how to make a few really good meals to sources of wisdom for challenging times).

# Chapter Seven

# Roots and Spirit: Honoring the Past, Bringing it Forward

## *Why Don't You Go into Real Estate?*

"You like the land, why don't you go into real estate?"

Considering that this question was asked of Ricky by his mother Sue when he was compelled to farm as a young man, it was remarkable that years later she sent a copy of *Time* magazine with the phrase 'local or organic?' on the cover. The times had changed in many ways. When we started farming, the mainstream was laughing down the possibility that this movement would ever take off. It was also meaningful that Ricky's mom was eventually able to understand and affirm her youngest son's career choice, if even through the sensationalized lens of main-stream media. We are not from farm families or from the community where we put down roots. So we are often asked 'how did you get into this?' by the curious reflecting on their own lives, or the young wondering how to break the news to their own parents that at the culmination of their college career they are going to turn to the land to eke out a livelihood.

Ricky and I had similar cultural roots (Jewish, New York metro-politan), but our family experiences were different in terms of class and ideology. Ricky's great-grandparents were among the early Jewish immi-grants to New York, his father's side in banking and mother's in a shel-lac business for which they traveled to India in the early- to mid-1900s many times. Although they became successful, 'No Jews Allowed' signs still blocked some of their attempts at assimilation. Ricky's father John (JB) took on embedded grief after his mother left the family followed by his father's early death. JB left Cobleskill College where he was studying dairy farming to go to World War II. After seeing what he saw and feel-ing what he did in the Philippines—the un-acknowledged PTSD of that era—he couldn't return to school, and joined his wife's family business importing shellac. Salesman by day, his only connection to farming was through his horse and the local stable. And while he was able to say it to others but not Ricky, JB was proud of his son's farming path, his own unanswered dream pursued if vicariously.

My parents were first-generation Russian and Turkish Jews, both coming from poor families in the Bronx. My maternal grandparents ran a basement laundry where my mother Miriam studied while sitting on piles of pressed sheets. My Dad, Stan—the youngest of eight—suffered with asthma that kept him out of the war. They were both accepted into City College, bastion of free higher education that enabled thousands of first-generation immigrants to move from poverty to professions (social worker and professor, respectively). I was named for my paternal grandmother Letaru, a fiery woman who ran a modest gambling ring out of ever-changing Bronx apartments. But rather than carrying on this tradition, I leaned towards that of my maternal grandmother, who tended houseplants on window ledges and identified sidewalk trees in their Rockaway housing project. A real estate career was not suggested by my socialist-leaning, politically-charged parents; they might have preferred I become and perhaps marry a university-tenured radical.

As the youngest of four, by the time Ricky came along his parents had already been through a number of draft-dodging, pot-smoking, mantra-chanting-induced parental panic attacks. My parents took a different route, not marrying until their early thirties—old for those times. Both of my parents pursued graduate degrees and my mother had (and continues to have) an especially politically active life. Called to testify before the House Committee on Un-American Activities, it wasn't until she had her second of three kids that the FBI stopped following her, knocking on the doors of our home, and putting spies in her workplaces. While Ricky likely picked up some of his work ethic from his father (who also berated him anytime he moved a workbench tool), my initial encounters with hands-on labor came through a semi-collective summer living experiment among my parents and three other couples. Together they bought a cabin and land for $12,000, dug a well, made a giant garden, and let their kids roam wild each summer.

We were both born in 1962, the year Rachel Carson's *Silent Spring* was published and on the later edge of the baby boomer generation, the air thick with marches and activism as we rode the tail end of the hippie tides. Into adulthood we went. We'd not yet met, but were each simultaneously drawn to environmentalism and with it, activism and a collective consciousness. It was an exciting era: full of promise, new legislation, and the birth of a plethora of visionary organizations, then small enough to foster a paradigm of cooperative work for the common good. With few informal programs, let alone sustainable agriculture majors in colleges at that time, we each sought and pursued a collage of mentors, self-education through books, and jobs to gather—over a decade or so—the farming and building skills that we would eventually shape into a not-quite-homesteading, not-quite-communal, and not-quite-poor existence, with our food, shelter, and energy needs met to create a beautiful life.

Like other first- and second-generation Jews, we wonder if these experiences as the children of those uprooted through the Jewish Diaspora help explain some things. Are our persevering ways born of a sense of survival and resilience carried forward from a people persecuted for millennia? Now with relative privilege in terms of class, education, and race—and with the ancestral traumas of peasant life and eviction from homelands several generations in the past—is the desire to re-root a form of generational healing? Yet, as people of a diaspora we find ourselves on the original land of the Nipmuc and other indigenous tribes. Feeling and knowing this, we honor our ancestors and the indigenous inhabitants of these lands, past and present. We do our best to steward this land now, and some day will pass it forward to those who we hope will care for it well.

## *Locked Behind the Gates of Hell*

In December of 1994, at the beginning of our eight-month pilgrimage, we lit our Hanukkah candles at the gates of hell: the entry to Auschwitz. As part of the convocation that initiated the walk, we spent a week there, sleeping each night in a converted building in what had been the concentration camp. Deb and I shared a room with an eclectic, beautiful being named Jhos (whose stories could fill a whole book) along with the other walkers. As I write this and try to imagine our room and the whole scene, I can't believe we did it, let alone were able to sleep in that place of such horrors.

It was very cold. Each morning at 5:00 A.M. we would hear the scraping of a shovel on frozen earth as it picked up another scoop of coal to feed the fires. Just writing that freaks me out as I recall thinking that it could have been that guy's father feeding the chambers with coal to burn my murdered ancestors. We would awaken soon after and join the others for an hour of prayer each morning. A dozen monks and nuns among us dry fasted the entire week of the convocation, spending each day sitting on the earth between the railroad tracks, chanting namu myoho renge kyo, the ancient mantra from the *Lotus Sutra*. As for the rest of us, we would spend the time chanting in prayer with them by the tracks, or walking around in a state of bewilderment and often overcome with grief at what we were seeing and feeling.

While there, I had a memory of sitting in my car a few years beforehand, soon after the sudden death of my friend Daisy. At the time I couldn't cry. I hadn't been able to cry over much throughout my life. Then one afternoon while roaming alone through what was now the Auschwitz museum (but had been a bunker), I meandered into a room that was full of suitcases from the former prisoners. The name "Ludwig Israel Baruch #1555" was written on one of the suitcases.

I saw my family name on a suitcase in Auschwitz, possessions never again held by their owner. In a state of shock I wandered around and lost track of time. It started to get dark. Meanwhile, the heavy gates to the part of the museum where I entered had been locked. I, Richard Schwab Baruc, the 'h' at the end of my name taken through assimilation, was locked in the camp. After some time, I found a spot where I was able to crawl my way out through the narrow space between the fence and the earth.

The next day, Deb and I stopped at a hollow on the concentration camp grounds. It was filled with cattails and there was a sign stating that this pit was filled with ashes removed from the chambers. My floodgates opened in a cathartic experience of deep crying. I did not grow up in a family of Holocaust survivors, or with anyone who had shared with me what remains unspeakable. I grieved in a deep ancestral way, far beyond what my mind had known. I cried until there was no energy left in me. This was but Day Six of an eight-month journey that would take us to places such as Palestine, Israel, Iraq, India, and Vietnam, where the tears would continue to flow.

One day many years later, I journeyed back in my mind to that moment I saw my family name among the murdered. When Levi was born, we added the 'h' back onto his name, a simple yet powerful act of reclaiming lineage and loss. When I paused from my workday on the farm as the universe brought me back to the experience of Auschwitz, I knew Levi was old enough to hear the story. I retrieved the photo I had taken of the pile of suitcases including #1555, inserted in an album and stored in his closet. We would later sit on his bed together to look at it as I shared the story.

Since that time, through his coming of age, and now in young adulthood, I have shared with Levi the many times in my life that have changed me. I have shared openly, through conversation and letters, how hard it is at times to survive physically and emotionally. I have shared as well my recognition of how I, like all, contribute to damage and suffering in some way. I've shared my daily quest to stay awake and not drop into complacency while living in a society that often tries to normalize and silence all of these feelings, especially among men. From the moment in Auschwitz when I saw the murder of my people in bold letters on a suitcase atop a massive pile, I have been able to cry for the magnitude of suffering that continues to exist. Unlike many others, I was able to crawl out from under the gates of hell physically, and knew then, as well as years later when I passed the story to my son, that I must keep doing so in my heart, conscience, and actions.

## *Privilege and Passport Stamps*

"We are global citizens," insisted one of the members of our pilgrimage as she presented her very unofficial 'global citizen' passport to the guard at the border between Israel and Jordan. The guard did not look amused as he adjusted his submachine gun replete with mega-rounds of artillery across his broad chest. In line behind them, I waited with Ricky, somewhere on a continuum between total embarrassment and mild terror. I understood the concept of 'oneness' she was trying to convey, but not only was it not working, it was also potentially dangerous to drag our entire pilgrimage group along on an experiment infused with white, Global North privilege.

As I sweat in the midday 95 degree heat beneath my best effort at modest Middle East travel wear, I hoped the rest of us would not be seen as off our rockers and subsequently denied access across the border to Jordan and then Iraq beyond. We were there to see for ourselves and then report back what the media did not convey about the impact and terror left in the wake of the Gulf War. On that day in 1995, we did not realize that there was so much more to come.

My turn in line came. I extended my own blue passport, the third I'd had in my adult life and already full of stamps. I had not had a problem receiving it or the ones before. I was aware of the benefit and privilege this provided, should we ever need to get the heck out of Dodge. Other than a few extra glances at my Middle-Eastern last name Habib, with this small paper booklet and the number assigned I had moved through many airports and borders, created copies to receive subsidized health insurance, used it as ID for bank loans and college financial aid, and other assorted needs from which those without documents are excluded. We had just left Gaza, and had been to many refugee camps throughout the West Bank. For thousands of people in the lands we had moved through, a passport proclaiming their identity as Palestinian would provide the ability to further their education, work, travel, and pass on these opportunities to their children without scrutiny and grave danger. That is still a daily personal and political hope.

Upon entering Israel a month prior and with the unknowns of the border crossings to come afterwards, we had given great thought to whether or not to have the Israeli stamp emboldened in our passport. Concerned that it might impact our passage into Jordan and Iraq and without allegiance to the political border it now represented, the stamp went on our temporary landing visas instead. And, while our cultural identity as Jews in the Diaspora was strong, we held more questions than connection to the political definition of Israel. We had begun the pilgrimage in Auschwitz and wailed deep despair for unspeakable torture of our own along with those with disabilities, political dissenters, gays and lesbians, and the Roma people.

We were Jews in the Diaspora of Ashkenazi and Sephardic descent; the Yiddish and Ladino languages that my grandparents carried as immigrants to the United States were in danger of being lost. Before rejoining the pilgrimage in the Holy Land, Ricky and I had spent a couple of weeks on an unplanned diversion to Turkey, where half of my family tree had spent the better part of 500 years. From Istanbul (where some family still remained) to the agricultural fields we visited, I felt a powerful, cellular memory. Our subsequent time reunited with the group and walking through the Holy Land was provocative as we sought to integrate the complex history, remapping of multiple political lines of Israel, visits to refugee camps, and conversations with peacemakers in Israel, the West Bank, and Gaza. Walking in the Holy Land did not produce, in my heart or soul, a deeper sense of connection with Israel as a Jew, although it strengthened a sense of connection to my roots and ancestors, primarily by staying the course of human rights and justice for all. Being in Israel soon after Auschwitz compounded questions and emotions, rekindled life experiences of suffering anti-Semitism, and raised questions about how to express our Jewish identity in more meaningful and conscious ways in our lives together forward.

When I was in college, I visited the Philadelphia Main Line with a close friend who was raised there. We had left college together after two years, and were saying goodbye to her mother before packing our bikes on a plane to ride throughout England and France for a few months.

"I don't think your mother likes me," I said after a not-so-warm welcome.

"It's not that she doesn't like you...it is just that you are 'a little too ethnic' for her." Hmmm. My New Jersey town of upbringing was a multi-class mix of Blacks, Jews, White Catholics, Puerto Ricans, and Greeks—diverse, but not harmonious. My parents were secular progressive Jews, and active in anti-racism work in our town. We didn't go to temple and I knew not one prayer and did not have a Bat Mitzvah. But they had co-founded a Community Jewish Sunday school where, each week, parents ate bagels and analyzed literature and current social issues while us kids learned what were probably cool things from young, hip Jewish teachers that I don't really remember. I was aware of being midway on the skin color continuum reflected in my town, but I'd never been described as "too ethnic." It was also my first time meeting old-money white people like my new friend's family.

At age thirteen a mole-like dot appeared in the middle of my forehead, a natural bindi of sorts. This, along with my olive skin and wide nose sometimes brought inquisitive glances. In the U.S., the curious and geographically challenged might say "You're *something*, right?" Traveling in Europe, India and Nepal in my early twenties, I'd be asked if I was from Brazil, or Morocco. I went to Cuba in 1989 and 1991 (the first time in order to be in the Cuban Socialist Circus, a story for another time). I saw some kindred mixes of others in the Diaspora, Cuba being one of the landing points for some Jews forced from Spain 500 years earlier. But for the fast-paced Spanish I felt another sense of home similar to what I would feel in Turkey a few years later. But I was born with white privilege on stolen land and held a passport in my bag granted by colonizers, while those then under sanctions in Cuba fingered their ration cards while standing on lengthy food lines, a daily act that would continue through the Special Period and before the re-advent of sustainable agriculture by necessity.

I held my passport of unearned privilege as our pilgrimage group was allowed to pass through the checkpoint between the West Bank and Jordan. That night, sleeping on the floor of a school in Amman that had been offered to our group, I unpacked the items in my knapsack. I reached for a small roll wrapped several times in a plastic bag. Seeds, collected from the markets of Turkey where my father's people had been for 500 years—since their own expulsion from Spain and until my grandparents made it to Ellis Island amid restrictive quotas limiting those of Eastern and Southern European descent. Did they carry, like so many immigrants and refugees then and now, seeds along with their few photos—if they even had the chance to gather anything before departure? My people had fled an agrarian past for a new life. They had not fully realized a life of freedom and prosperity themselves, but their sacrifices and efforts propelled their dream forward for their children and grandchildren like me. I fingered a flattened white squash seed, a speckled bean, and something tiny from a plant resembling arugula in our bag of seeds collected from the farmers of the world. I would be able to transport these without worry that they would be lost or taken on dangerous border crossings. I would be able to grow and share these without fear that they were my only link to feeding my family.

Years before the pilgrimage, and before the personal soul-searching journeys that took me across many borders and lands, we had that garden at New Alchemy where we had painted, "This Garden is grown in Solidarity with Those Around the World Helping to Feed the People." Ricky and I didn't know then that the raised bed, hand labor, small plot, and simple tool methods of the peasants we encountered in Turkey, India, Thailand, and Vietnam would so inform our ways and our ability to sow seeds of solidarity. We are grateful for the soil into which to place our hands and seeds—the soil we call home—and give thanks for the sacrifices and journeys made by our ancestors.

## The Mesas of My Mind

I had disappeared. Or at least, the Ricky who listened to the news each morning then rock and roll throughout the day farming had vanished. Instead, CD after CD of readings and lectures from a host of spiritual teachers now played continuously for days and weeks on end as I hauled wheelbarrows of compost and sowed bed after bed of salad greens. Instead of the latest music, the air reverberated with messages like "you are here to enable the divine purpose of the universe ...you are not your mind...nothing exists outside the now."

This was certainly not a planned part of my farming journey, but an abrupt detour that almost derailed our marriage because Deb was confused and unsettled by what was happening. Yet it saved my ass, and enabled me to continue farming by feeding my worn spirit and body, and awakening to other parts of myself.

In retrospect, I was more worn out than I realized. In December 2006, we took a family vacation to the Southwest. We visited a friend in Tucson and toured Arcosanti, Paolo Soleri's visionary community we'd long read about, followed by some beautiful hikes in Sedona, before winding our way to the Grand Canyon. After a night there, we made our way through a snowstorm towards the Hopi lands. We spent our first night at a Hopi-run motel on the Second Mesa, enjoying traditional lamb and posole stew. The next morning we made our way to Walpi, the oldest continuously inhabited native village in North America. A young Hopi woman gave us a tour while the elders were belowground in the kiva for their winter solstice ceremonies.

Something happened to me there. I now have more words to describe what I felt then. It was as if my ancient self was tuning into this energy coming from belowground, something that I had not yet experienced in this incarnation.

The internal churning inside of me continued as we drove from Walpi to the Abiquiu landscape of Northern New Mexico. Abiquiu is a small village with its own powerful energy and a rich history, home of Georgia O'Keeffe and the inspiration for so many artists past and present. We rented a small cottage from a wonderful Mexican-American couple, just outside of town in an old Hispanic hamlet called Barranca on the Chama River. They had worked for O'Keeffe and at Los Alamos, where the first nuclear bombs were detonated. Getting to know this wonderful couple added story and humanity to Georgia O'Keeffe's stunning art.

We had left New England for a bit of reprieve from winter, but of course it had followed us. On what was to be our third and last day there, we were asked by our new friends Hector and Alina to help bring in the horses from a nearby ranch as the snow was coming down fast, and not stopping any time soon. Deb, Levi (then seven), and I made our way to the paddock as Hector told us to try to herd four somewhat wild horses towards the trailer. They needed to be moved out of the field before the snow was too deep for any of us to move. It was a wild adventure of the power of nature that was fitting right in with the energy of our trip. The horses were very high-strung and we tried our best to get them into the trailer. After a few hours they were in and we were off. Hector drove us in his truck at high speed down a narrow and winding ranch road to break a path through the snow while we still could, truck and trailer sliding from one side of the road to the other. This day was a thriller and Levi's young self was surely wondering what his crazy parents had got him into this time. Meanwhile, the snow continued for the next forty-eight hours, and our plans to go to Ojo Caliente and Santa Fe were thwarted as all highways in New Mexico closed for their biggest storm in fifty years.

We were stuck in Barranca with the power going on and off and our modest staples running out as we'd only planned on being there two days, not five. Hector and Alina were expecting family that couldn't make it due to the storm, so we created an 'instant family' for a few meals with them. Levi and Deb played board games and I sunk into a book I'd happened to bring, *The Earth Knows My Name*. This proved to be a pivotal moment for me, and right on the heels of my experience on the Hopi Mesas. Each chapter described a different farmer and their relationship to land and culture. One focused on Whit Davis, a Rhode Island corn farmer who continued to grow the traditional flint corn (for cornmeal and johnnycakes) that his family had received from the Narragansett tribe many years before—and had kept growing it for ten generations. He was the one who returned the seed to the Wampanoag tribe. Interspersed in Whit's story were some very powerful tales of the mistreatment of the native peoples by white settlers. I had read many accounts of the genocide of Native Americans but this time all of the energy swirling inside me from the journey, combined with a realization hit me, and hit me hard. It was as if a lightning bolt had struck me with an intense, essential question: *How is my mind different than the white man's mind that caused so much havoc and destruction to the indigenous people of this land?* The question was seared into my psyche as it repeated itself over and over again in my head. It was a question that would catapult me into my spiritual journey and begin to unravel the easygoing but rock and roll Ricky that Deb once knew.

Here I was, an organic farmer living off-the-grid. But increasingly in the last year or two, I had been waking up each morning in fear, stress, and anxiety. What was the mindset of the whites that arrived here in 1491 that resulted in the sense of entitlement and power that led to the genocide of Indigenous peoples? Yes, I was living the green dream, but what was actually going on inside my head? What effect did my colonized and colonizer mind have on me and everyone and everything around me?

When I returned back to our farm, these essential questions blared in my head over and over, mixed with contemplations of midlife, and were amplified by the energy I picked up in Walpi while the elders were in ceremony. I was in for a big transition. The project I was working on at the time was building the second floor onto our produce wash area to become apprentice housing, a space that would later be known as the treetop loft. Normally I would crank music while working, but something possessed me to pull out Eckhart Tolle's *The Power of Now* audiobook that our previous year's farm apprentice Caroline had left. Each day while working, I listened to Tolle (or 'ET,' as Deb would call him) over and over again. It was total immersion into the only spiritual teacher on tape that I had at the time. I now see this phase as an initial deprogramming stage. I was deprogramming from growing up in a culture of insanity, and going AWOL from a fast-paced, stress-inducing, consumer-focused way of life. By listening to these teachings I realized I was not alone, and not the only one feeling this way. There was another way to be on this planet.

What is it that coalesces in one's life in order to make big changes? What brings the pieces into alignment to create the perfect storm for change? For some folks change may be gradual, and for others, like myself, it's an abrupt shift. To break an addiction—be it drugs, alcohol, or a crazed mind—an intense experience is often needed to break the patterns we are stuck in. This was all a very difficult and trying time on our marriage and I thank my loving partner Deb for hanging in there and being so supportive through it all. It was a baptism by fire. During this transitional time, Deb would sometimes say, "I love the Ricky I married," and I would reply, "you can have that Ricky—I can't live with him anymore."

Years later, I understood that I had had a great deal of negative thinking playing out inside my head. By listening to another voice on repeat that offered a more enlightened way of thinking, my negative thoughts could not get a word in edgewise. They simply couldn't get through. I borrowed and bought more CDs—Pema Chodron, Don Miguel Ruiz, Michael Beckwith—and their words became my new language. I was reassessing and reconnecting to my true self, and reprogramming to repair the societal damage I had embodied. As my dear friend Carlos, a psychologist, describes, I had 'spiritual dyslexia:' I could no longer read myself or trust my thoughts. Old internal 'tapes' were taking me down, and it was literally listening to new tapes that allowed me to re-emerge. A close friend in my men's group who went through similar healing processes from a traumatic childhood experience shared with me that the Navajo people will tell (sometimes for a week straight!) their creation stories of awakening and rebirth to a tribe member returning from battle or other traumatic experiences.

The process of listening to spiritual teachings all day, every day while hauling compost, sowing seeds, or banging nails for a farm building went on for two years. During that time I developed a daily practice and started each day with an hour of meditation, which I continue today. From there on, it became about watching my mind all day, so that meditation became a twenty-four-hour practice. Soon I no longer needed the recorded messages of others to replace the negative voices in my head, and could enjoy the quiet while working. I listened to the plants more fully than ever. In alignment with my personal shift, our farm apprenticeship process changed too, in that I sought and attracted young people interested not only in the physical work of growing food, but also spiritual growth. I had contacted Whit Davis by phone after coming home from that trip to New Mexico and we had a wonderful connection. He sent me some Narragansett corn seed. Many years later I continue to grow the ancestral corn of this land along with other traditional varieties—including that of the Hopi—to eat and share. Many traditions say that "corn is life." I'm sure that connecting with this ancient plant had an impact on my healing process.

It was not easy for me to find farmers who were both connected to working the land and also were spiritual seekers. Then, one evening, I called a garlic farmer in Wisconsin who was referred to me by another grower, knowing he had some seed to sell. Jason and I began easily chatting away about his agricultural community and the Amish women who worked on his farm. It all sounded like a pretty unique place and I was inquisitive as I respect the Amish work ethic and lifestyle. During our conversation he must have felt I was an open individual and he began to share with me spiritual stuff he was into. He told me about a woman named Barbara Marciniak who channeled a collective of beings from the star cluster Pleiades. Years before, this conversation would have most likely been just too far out for me, and just not my thing. To this day I still don't know why it resonated with me as I had absolutely no context for a collective of beings from another star system. Not only did I listen, but also immediately ordered a quarterly newsletter called *The Pleiadian Times*. Either divine intervention or meditation had been preparing me for situations where I would not react in the same old way. Much of the teachings I'd been listening to brought forward ancient wisdom, but I had not considered learning from other beings.

While I continue to seek, read, and listen to spiritual teachings from human and nonhuman beings, I have a different consciousness than when I began this journey. I took a leap from living with my mind controlling my day, to where I am now: living from the heart. While local food consumers seem to like the idea of their farmer working sunup to sundown to grow their vegetables, it is not, never has been, and never will be sustainable. Many farmers I've known have killed relationships or dropped from exhaustion. If we seek balance in the soil, we must also find balance in our lives.

## From Varanasi Ghats to Wrestling Mats

One of the things we give the teens in our SOL Garden program is a small card with ten ideas for personal health and resilience. Rather than a typical 'what not to do' list of sex and drugs, we share in our conversation circle what each of us *can* do to promote wellbeing. Among the suggestions are a contemplative or movement practice, a few trusted friends, and some gentle natural remedies for self-care. Yoga has been a vital part of my life, providing much life wisdom and tools for health, a common space where I have met some of my closest friends, and teachings that I have been able to share in service to others.

The pull to travel to Europe and India had been hovering for a long time, and in my early twenties (the mid-1980s), I counted out my waitress tips that I'd been stuffing in a coffee can for a year and bought a plane ticket, leaving New Alchemy and Ricky for an adventure of the spirit.  Plans to travel all year with a friend shifted after a two-month bicycling trip in England and France—the first phase of this yearlong journey—and I was left to figure out how to spend the next eight months alone. I had recently begun doing some yoga postures as described in *Light on Yoga*. While in London and preparing to journey to India, I called the B. K. S. Iyengar center figuring I'd simply show up in Pune, India, but the Brits snootily informed me there was a several-year waiting list.

I went to India anyway and found myself in Goa, where European teachers offered some free yoga classes on the beach for the stoned and the seekers. It was enough to slightly increase my vocabulary of asanas (postures), and I practiced these for the next six months whether I was awakening in the holy city of Varanasi or stretching after a day of walking in the Himalayas.

I moved to Western Massachusetts in 1987, soon after returning from travels. India was still fresh in my heart and amoebas still lurking in my gut when I picked up Adam hitchhiking. He was housesitting for friends who were, in fact, studying with Iyengar in Pune! Conversation turned quickly to my recent travels, arrival in Western Mass, and desire to find a yoga teacher to pick up where I'd left off in the Himalayas. He said he would call me when his friend Eddie returned from India. I didn't imagine that he would, or that this encounter would lead to finding my teacher, a community of friends, a strong practice—and later, teaching.

Upon his return from India, Eddie Modestini warmly invited me to show up for his UMass classes, which I did faithfully twice a week, receiving his generosity and mentoring. We didn't even have yoga mats, just a worn red wrestling mat over a linoleum floor of the basement in one of the University gyms, cinderblock walls a semi-gloss yellow. Where the mat wasn't dusty it was deeply sweat-stained. It was a totally imperfect space for a most wonderful and deep immersion into the practice of yoga.

I began attending Eddie's evening classes, too, where he and his then-wife Deb, along with Adam, Marilyn, Mary, Lee, Sully, and a few others would practice, then go out to Amherst Chinese for the best mung bean sprouts (with ginger soy sauce) on the East Coast. Several in this group would remain my lifelong friends. We made many trips to Boston for intensives with senior Iyengar teachers, and Eddie and Deb hosted several, too. Eddie was very knowledgeable about anatomy and brilliant at sequences, so I gained a strong foundation. He invited me to assist his UMass classes, and then eventually take these over when their marriage ended and he left the area. I will be ever-grateful for his generosity; he mentored me for several years and trusted me to teach when I could not have otherwise afforded to study or train. My hours on the mat and the pure spirit of his mentoring likely surpassed today's multi-thousand-dollar teacher trainings.

Yoga has remained the primary practice in my resilience toolbox for many decades. I am more comfortable with moving meditations, like yoga and dance, than with sitting. I did submerse myself in a ten-day silent Vipassana retreat as well as years of dance and other forms of body-mind explorations, but my yoga practice is what stays and what grounds me. Another wonderful teacher, Sam, and new friends have become a great middle-life sangha. The mat I keep rolled up near the woodstove helps me to greet most days with Sun Salutations, and end days with some centering or restorative postures once dinner is on the stove for my family.

I never sought to teach yoga as a profession or livelihood, but the spirit of generosity through which I was introduced to yoga stayed with me. Any teaching I've done over the years has been in community settings—for UMass and high school students, as a benefit for food co-op members and free classes for people in recovery, as well as yoga woven into gardening and other types of classes we teach.

In addition to asana (posture) and pranayama (breath and life force), the yoga sutras provide a lens for being, action, and how to live a meaningful life. The first two of the eight limbs of yoga are fundamental ethical precepts called yamas and niyamas. These are concerned with how we express our energy in relation to others. They imply that our fundamental nature is compassionate, generous, honest and peaceful, collectively forming a universal morality. For example, of the yamas, ahimsa is non-violence, and implies proactive kindness and thoughtful consideration. Satya, or commitment to truthfulness, is a precept based on the belief that honest communication and action are at the foundation of healthy relationships, communities, and governments, and that deliberate mistruth causes harm. These and the other yamas offer wisdom towards a more conscious life and lifestyle. The niyamas are more intimate in nature, and form our personal code for living soulfully with such themes as contentedness, inquiry, self-awareness, and celebration of the spiritual. Yoga has been a gift and a guide. It has been personally grounding, a tool for self-care, and a way of serving others. It provides a way for me to come back to center again and again in the midst of a full life.

## Rituals of a Farmer

The growing seasons filled with trial and tribulation, experiment and wonder are great teachers. Finding balance as a farmer, father, partner, and artist is an ongoing quest that becomes clearer with time and age.

### My Day Begins

I wake up at 5 A.M. three mornings a week, not to move irrigation pipe or open a computer as many farmers do, but to get in a workout to keep me in shape as a physically engaged farmer, as well as to clear my head. Otherwise, my brain tries to fill with questions like *When will rain come?* or spin the old mental tapes of *Am I doing enough?*

I get the family up at 6:15 a.m., then neaten up from the night before. Deb does the cooking in the house and I do the dishes. In the

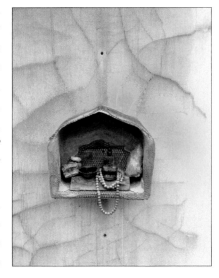

years before he started driving and then went to college, I would drop our son Levi off at the bus stop, where we enjoyed a few moments of father-son conversation before I headed to meditate with our neighbor Stefan from 7:00 A.M. to 8:00 A.M. I am sorry if this breaks the image for many of 'their local farmer' beginning the workday well before dawn to pick and pack crops for farmers' markets. I've done that. But if I had not started meditating, I might not be here now to grow food for my customers, let alone be happily married and a father who has spent quality time with his son. While I was long-drawn to spiritual and philosophical teachings, I actually began a regular meditation practice with one of our apprentices who had done a meditation course prior to arriving, and I have been going strong since. At that time in my life I felt it would be good to make some time for meditation. Today I couldn't imagine my life without that morning hour, to totally remove myself from the physical world, clear my mind from the nonstop whirlwind of thoughts, and help me be more open to what the universe has to offer.

After my morning meditation, and if it is during the growing season, I harvest some kale and spinach for our green drink smoothie. I find Deb preparing for her day, often after some morning yoga. The sun is out and the solar electric system is charging up for maximum power. The dogs look at us longingly for a potential walk (that they will soon get). The fresh greens go into the Vitamix with fruit or maple syrup, nut butter, and hemp oil or aloe. Having a green drink daily gives me the confidence that I am getting enough nutrition into my body, along with drinking enough water through the day. Deb and I joke we are going to live to 100 if the Vitamix holds out.

## Smoke Signals and Little Black Books

I do not use a computer, but I plan each week—and then each day—to the hour. I don't use a computer or cell phone, so friends often joke that smoke signals are the way to reach me. For big picture organizing, research, and bookkeeping, I keep notebooks for all aspects of the farm as well as the other realms of my life on my desk. But on a day-to-day basis I rely on the little black books that I keep in my overall pockets. When I am outside on the land, many of my inspirational thoughts flow, so I carry one small black book to capture these thoughts. My other black book is for the to-do list. I also have several larger sheets with farm planning, and a number of folders and notebooks to keep track of crops. I always have at least four colors of highlighters on hand to code projects, and for a favorite activity—to cross completed tasks off of the to-do lists.

### Balance and Handwork

My ideal weeks are organized and balanced like this: Monday, Tuesday, and Wednesday are for farming all day or farming-related building projects. Thursday is for our SOL Garden youth program April through summer, and Fridays are for art and woodworking, or making something beautiful to enhance the land. I stock our solar-powered farm stand several times a week, and make one weekly delivery to our local food co-op. In the days when we had multiple apprentices, I was farming every day, as we grew lots of greens and were doing two deliveries a week to restaurants and co-ops that took many hours and got me home late and ragged at night. After my years of farming in New York State including full weekends at the Greenmarkets in NYC and Ithaca farmers' markets, I wanted my weekends free to do other life projects.

Apprentices brought high moments and low moments, but towards the end of those ten years I realized I was doing less of what I loved and more of organizing the work for the crew, and cherished when I was alone to plant by myself. Since, I've developed techniques for farming so that I can grow lots of food without machinery and basically as a one-person operation (except on Tuesdays when we welcome volunteers, and during the garlic harvest when more labor is needed). No-till techniques are better for the land *and* they are better for my psyche. As my time is not spent tilling or weeding and with much less watering due to no-till farming practices, I can focus on seedling production and successive sowings, plant and soil health, and harvesting. All that microbial and worm activity going on under the cardboard fills the plants with prana, or life force. A balanced week helps me recharge my own prana, too.

## *Planting as Ceremony:*

Each time I plant some seeds, I make an offering at one of our altars in front of the greenhouse, to take a moment to make a prayer to give thanks, and to simply stop and marvel at the magical process of a living seed that is about to begin. I have used various seeders along the way, but to this day I count on the most excellent germination by scatter sowing (or broadcasting) seeds with a small, non-mechanical, hand seedsower. Before I do a planting, I put some seeds from that variety under my tongue for ninety seconds or so before I put them onto the soil. This ritual came to me from *The Ringing Cedars of Russia* book series out of Siberia: the idea is to let the soil know what I need, what I am lacking nutritionally—which is hopefully universal enough to benefit many others, too. This is a great practice and why we are such advocates of people growing their own food to build their own connection with their land. Humans could not have survived this long without such an intimate relationship with the earth and a deep communication with the natural world. A deep connection to the earth is held deeply in our individual and collective consciousness; for many, it has been sitting latent or erased through schooling and societal messages.

I love growing greens. With good compost and proper watering, I have gotten over sixteen harvests from a single planting of one of my favorite lettuce varieties called "Outredgeous." There is always a succession of greens in different stages of growth. The greens have been, and remain to be, the most time-intensive part of the operation. I still love it, this weekly ritual, and there is nothing like a fresh salad from newly harvested greens. Back in the day we would load up our F-350 and go off for a four-hour journey delivering up to fourteen accounts to restaurants and food co-ops. After ten years, plus another ten before that driving to markets, I became a ghost on this delivery route and it was time to sell completely locally. It was a hard choice to make as my greens were very popular and I could have expanded. But I was shriveling up inside. That is why I now grow greens for just our local food co-op and for our farm stand. People were skeptical that customers would show up at an out-of-the-way farm stand on Chestnut Hill Road. I am grateful for and amazed by the number of people that do. Each day from April through November, I fill the solar-powered refrigerator in our farm stand with fresh greens. I appreciate all of our customers and especially enjoy those that don't fit the stereotypical 'greens eating' type. From our UPS driver who picks up a bag after each of his deliveries to the guy that hauls old metal junk, the farm stand feeds a variety of people, including those with little money but who know what is right and important. Now that our neighbors Bruce and Rachel have a goat milk dairy stocked with yogurt, cheeses, and grass-fed meats, our farm stands have become community resources for health and vitality, and a great way to educate the public about food and nutrition.

## Farm as Gathering Place

It is heartwarming to know that many who spent time on our farm continue to incorporate no-till farming techniques learned, and equally important, that they cultivate self-care and healthy relationships. It required a lot of time to manage apprentices—even the best of them—and as happens with farmers (or with any business), as the system gets larger and more complex, you can find yourself distanced from the origins and practices that attracted you in the first place. Instead of having two apprentices intensively for six months, I now welcome volunteers on Tuesdays, which turns the farm into a gathering place for that day. At the heart of my volunteer crew is a reliable and hardworking group of women over fifty who have really taken to no-till methods. Diane began coming after her retirement from the UMass facilities department and now has her own market garden and roadside stand. Ellen moved up from Tennessee and found us as part of her search for like-minded community.

The model of a weekly volunteer day also opens up new partnerships. For example, we collaborated with a local agency that provides adults with developmental and intellectual disabilities with job training and volunteerism through community engagement. After each visit, they brought food they helped grow back for lunch with others in their program. Our other farm volunteers enjoyed this fresh energy and the opportunity to interact in meaningful activity with people they would not get to otherwise. Tuesdays on the farm have become a special and manageable way to unite those diverse in age, interest, and ability and share some of our Grow Food Everywhere techniques with them, plus enjoy rich conversation over lunch. On the other days, I have some peaceful time farming with myself.

### Being Here Now

Much has evolved internally and externally over my three decades of farming. After farming 'organically' (but still with tractors, and not in a way that was humanly or environmentally sustainable) on my farm in upstate New York, I shifted to approach farming in a way that has always felt more right for me, using hand tools. Yet, my mind would still try to seduce me: *be like every-*  *one else, get a tractor, and go faster.* Finally, in my fifties, I've settled in to how I do it, and it feels right. In fact, I realized that if I over-manipulate the soil I am imposing a mindset of a colonizer, seeking to dominate rather than observe, respect, and honor in my participation with the soil as a farmer. This not only leads to healthier crops and soil, but as I work to decolonize my mindset and related ways of being as a farmer, I simultaneously shift my ways of being as a human. Having found my way of farming, one that keeps evolving with the years, there is such a special feeling, being and working on this piece of ground that fills me with joy and centeredness.

After thirty years of farming, I'm settled with my approach, staying focused on tasks not technology, and working at a pace that is humanly sustainable. In my twenties, thirties, and forties, I was always looking down the road. Then when I turned fifty, I shifted to being here now by farming in touch with the land and in active prayer as I feed the soil. Every shovelful of compost is food for the life in the soil. The mulch to keep life and garlic warm for the winter will also break down and feed the life in the soil, the microbes that will help plants take up the fertilizer more efficiently.

Yes, the world around me is in utter chaos. In the old days, I'd spend my day mulling that over, pretty pissed off. But these days I'm ready for a different consciousness, a different way of being: a reality that I believe in, that I want to live in right now. Here I am, a Sephardic Ashkenazi Jew on the land of the Nipmuc people, seeking to be and farm the land in a sacred manner. Mahatma Gandhi said, "My life is my message." While pushing a wheelbarrow filled with compost, with my mind clear and the sun out, I'm fully alive. It is my life and my work all wrapped together. It is my message and my prayer.

## The Practice

Here I sit in the loft of a renovated barn that was at one point a rehearsal space for the rock band Aerosmith. Every morning I pull myself out of bed and walk my bleary-eyed self over to this space at our neighbor's place to meditate. When a practice such as meditation has saved your life, you don't question whether or not to throw the covers off. I get up, get over there, and sit for an hour.

Before I started meditating, I was ruled by my thoughts; whatever my morning thoughts were would dictate my mood for the day. I meditate to clear my head. It's like a reset button that gets me back to center, back to my authentic self. I meditate with two different neighbors, Stefan and Penelope, and when we are done we talk for a few minutes before we go off to our respective work as farmer, organ-builder/solar installer, and (now retired) social worker. One morning I shared with my fellow meditators how after all of these years of inner turmoil, I finally felt safe and at home—home being on planet Earth, and completely grounded. After day after day, year after year of sitting and meditating each morning, I no longer identify as a collection of delusional thoughts that keeps me running and running. I have finally found peace on planet Earth.

By quieting the unconstructive inner dialogue I've become more open to listening from within, and hearing what my ancestors, the star beings, and the unseen ones are telling me. The inner quiet brings me to a place of clarity so that I can begin to remember my original instructions. The words of the late, indigenous musician John Trudell struck me. He said that every one of us is a descendant of a tribe and that every one of us has a tribal ancestry and genetic memory. These words resonate deeply. For many years I'd been drawn to indigenous wisdom, as that which I learned through reading such teachings felt so right. If we each reach back far enough in our ancestry we would find earth-based values that are part of our own indigenous worldview. At what point in each of our histories were these values and beliefs taken from us and replaced with a belief system that was devoid of the wonder of the natural world?

There has been an increase in interest in no-till gardening and farming, and I've been asked to present more frequently on my practices and methods. I was invited to be part of a local library's panel on soil carbon restoration to reduce climate change, and knew I would be the opening speaker following some short films on the topic. As I prepared, I felt compelled to offer a different take on the no-till teachings I've developed on our farm. The issue at hand is so much deeper than techniques and methods. For many years I held the deep conviction and belief that it would be an environmental shift that would save the human race. When we first came to our land to initiate Seeds of Solidarity we focused on shaping integrated systems for food. Energy and shelter was aligned with this continued belief. We did create a place of beauty as well as an ecological oasis that we and others have come to love. And, over the years, and parallel to my own internal shift, I now realize it is a more comprehensive worldview that must change, and that continued environmental Band-Aid solutions will not result in deep change unless we each get to the root of our ills and recognize our disconnect from the earth and traditional belief systems. What keeps us from going deeply into some pivotal questions: is it too scary to look at ourselves to acknowledge as a species what we have done and continue to do to the earth and all life? Is it easier to just focus on yet another eco-solution to our devastated planet so that we don't have to look deep within? What is the role of privilege and power in wanting to focus on "green" solutions and then just keep moving forward rather than fully acknowledge the legacy of racial and other injustices of the past and of today?

As I prepare to share a presentation on farming, I contemplate how, in a loving, non-preaching way I can express to attendees the responsibility and passion I feel, informed by the wisdom of other teachers and elders that I have encountered. I can relate to inner experiences

of joy and harmony, suffering and disruption, and the co-existence of these. I want not only to teach gardening techniques, but also to share my reverence for the natural world verdant with life force, and how this awareness of life force heightens my own.

My meditation practice helps me to take more risks in presentations. In the tours we offer about food, farming, and land, it encourages me to be open and vulnerable, and to share my inner struggles and realizations. This is not often what people expect to hear from a man whose hands are calloused with thirty years of work on the land; they may expect that I will focus only on how-to techniques. But when I open my heart and inner work along with sharing gardening and farming practices, I often find that many are intrigued and relieved to hear that there can and must be many ways to think about our practice in order to connect with the land, and reconnect to our traditions and truest selves.

## Seeking the Sacred on the Farm

A walk on the Seeds of Solidarity path is often with purpose. A garden cart of seedlings to plant with our SOL Garden youth program, or produce to restock the solar-powered farm stand is hauled up amid conversation about the day. The cart is pulled down the path at the end of the day stacked with tools, muddied mail piled on top. This path connects farm fields with spaces for educational programs. It connects us with Chestnut Hill Road, where wonderful, eclectic neighbors have welcomed our efforts since we arrived decades ago with scythe, skills, and a vision.

Interspersed among gardens, greenhouses, and solar-powered buildings are sculptures and artistic altars, and words from those whose wisdom keeps the journey towards justice and freedom ever-alive. A colorful sign with a quote from indigenous elders reveals a planting of traditional Narragansett corn. Activist Angela Davis's photo graces one greenhouse and another honors United Farm Workers founder Cesar Chavez. The words of scientists and authors Rachel Carson and Vandana Shiva remind us what is important each time we enter the building that houses tools and seeds. An image of Martin Luther King Jr. with Thich Nhat Hanh between our art studio and group meeting space emanates compassionate conviction. Non-violent movements for social change past to present have inspired a visual timeline that honors acts of courage throughout history and today.

Years back, I was the one initially hesitant to dot our entire landscape with quotes and accompanying photos, for these are not the typical "Pick your own peas here" signs. We were and are a vegetable farm after all, and with several education programs for our North Quabbin community, plus visitors far and wide. But Ricky was inspired. And like most things he sets his mind to, once the idea took root, he went full steam ahead. His handcrafted signs with the words and likenesses of local and global visionaries and change-makers started cropping up as fast as the garlic and greens for which we were known.

The uncertainties of farming can make you feel vulnerable enough without also exposing heartfelt spiritual and moral leanings for anyone ambling down your farm drive to see. But we needed daily reminders of what passion and purpose look like from wise messengers—those who had gone before us in the struggles for social and environmental justice—and who had persevered far more than we had on even the hardest of times on the farm. In turn, our farm apprentices, interns, and thousands who visited Seeds of Solidarity over the years would get to consider much more than food and farming.

During a tour for a youth group from Worcester many years back we said, as we often say to visitors to our farm, "Walk around for five minutes and come back to the circle with something that catches your eye." Upon her return, a young woman offered, "I don't remember the words exactly, but it was about peace and love, and the guy's last name was Lama."

Cultivating values such as reverence, compassion, and justice and reflecting these in the visual fabric of our farm remains as much a part of our message as our no-till techniques, food justice efforts, and renewable energy landscape. We've come to learn that the walk up and down our farm road and throughout the fields is not just about what we do, but the creativity, connectedness, and reverence with which we do it. Words shared by an Iraqi man we met while there on our eight-month international pilgrimage remind us of the creative resilience of the human spirit. He said: "Even in times of war we still breathe and make art."

Ricky identifies as a land artist, both for the relationship he seeks to embody and impart as he farms, and because his experience as a builder led him to make furniture, meditation benches, altars and platters of local wood. He cuts standing dead cedar and gathers laurel from the forest for this craft. The wood is inlaid with symbolic designs made of crops from the

Winter is a good time to gather wood to be milled for furniture making.

Meditation benches combine Ricky's daily practice with his love of the woods and sacred crops he grows.

land such as blue corn, tobacco, and pepper, which have been crushed to resemble colorful stone. Our friend Terry Jenoure invited him to do a show at the Augusta Savage Gallery that she directs at UMass (named for the African American Harlem Renaissance sculptor). Being a modest guy, doing a show alone felt imposing. So we created a family show that ran during the winter of 2017. We filled the truck with maple slab tables with rustic birch legs, a chair crafted in the style taught to Ricky by Cayoni, and crates of 'illuminators'—lengths of saplings engraved with words such as 'awaken,' 'honor,' 'joy,' and 'trust,' topped with votive candles. Portfolios held art that would grace the walls, along with baskets of corn and sage from the farm. Terry instructed us to leave it all in the middle of the gallery floor, then kicked us out and worked her magic with her assistant, Alexia. At the opening, guests were surrounded by furniture Ricky crafted of trees from our land, my photos through the seasons and functional pottery, and Levi's mandalas and soil interpretation of a kolam, a geometric design drawn on the earth by women in many parts of India to bless the entry to a home. Visitors continued to add to the kolam, engaging with the space and art—palpable and beautiful energy to receive back upon gathering it all up to bring back to the farm.

Farming is beautiful and farming is hard. The seasons arrive with uncertainties of drought, sudden winds, snowy or snowless winters. The human-wreaked havoc of global warming is felt deeply by small farmers locally and globally. Of the 570 million farms in the world, 90 percent of these are run by individuals or families and feed the world on less than 25 percent of the world's arable farmland, according to the Food and Agriculture Organization of the United Nations. Many traditional and small farmers incorporate agroecological practices but are still vulnerable to radical changes in weather patterns and the perils of corporate agriculture such as seed supply and contamination of lands by GMOs. And still, the earth, seas, and forests provide such amazing bounty of wild food, cultivated food, and medicinal plants. In these times of such contradictions and urgency, it feels essential to keep our spirits strong, and to honor past, present and the unseen through contemporary ceremony and celebration on the farm.

We were not passed down land rituals from our people in the Jewish Diaspora. For many who were poor or persecuted, relinquishing or escaping an agrarian way of life was a priority. The ones we *have* been taught are most often through story and song, rather than direct connection on the land itself. Yet seeds, plants and soil contribute to our life force, and can reawaken connection to culture and place. For Ricky, it took twenty years of working with the land, working on himself, and support from dear friends to be ready to offer land ceremony. In trying times, it is increasingly essential to honor the ways of the original wisdom of the land, once known by our own ancestors and upheld by many indigenous farmers and fishermen around the world. How do we bring the deep spirit of food and farming into conversation and practice? How do we create contemporary land rituals and ceremonies, honoring diverse, wise, and deep traditions without appropriating from cultures of which we are not born?

Rather than initiate the spring planting with stress or fear of what may or may not come, we now begin the season at Seeds of Solidarity with an 'Awaken with the Land' gathering of friends and farmers, artists and musicians. Each year takes a slightly different form depending on who arrives and the traditions they bring. During one such ceremony, some walked the stone circle at the edge of our garlic field while others added natural and symbolic objects to a heart-shaped mandala. Our friend Ricardo invited song to Brazilian rhythms. Phyllis and Ricky encouraged offerings of meaningful words or gestures, and Carlos' meditations held the circle sweet and strong. Water gathered from the spring cascade at nearby Bear's Den so rich with native history was poured into unfired clay cups, then showered with

blessings on the fields. Nourishing food from winter stores and spring gardens was shared. There is no rigid script for these gatherings; it is beautiful to co-create in community.

Along with the artistic signs on our farm that remind us each day to stay focused bigger-picture and honor those who we admire as leaders and visionaries, daily rituals and contemplative practices provide emotional and spiritual balance to the intense physicality of this lifestyle. Particularly during the spring and summer months, it is common to hear the refrain from well-intentioned acquaintances or customers, "You must be really busy!" as if this is something to which we should aspire. It can be tempting to play into this massage for the ego. But, we really don't want to perpetuate the concept of busyness, or affirm that this is somehow representative of success. This busy mentality often comes with stress, poor health, or divorce. We especially don't want to model this for the rising generation of farmers. Our practices of meditation and yoga, of nurturing and prioritizing family time, quality friendships, and a loving relationship are as important to us to feed as the soil upon which we rely. In these times especially, we need more signs that remind us that love and compassion are among the values that not only keep us farming, but will also keep us all nourished for the road ahead.

*Field Guide Chapter Seven:*
*Roots and Spirit: Honoring the Past,*
*Bringing it Forward*

## Questions to Ponder: Traditions and Practices

- Do you have a spiritual practice of any kind? If so, where are you within your practice: evolving, content, complacent, stuck? If you do not and wish to, what are the barriers?

- What cultural or spiritual traditions have you carried on? Which have you reinterpreted? What would you like to learn about your ancestral past and traditions?

- How do you weave your ancestral roots and traditions with day-to-day life, or with your current spiritual and physical ways of being?

- How do, or do you hope to bring spiritual values into your home life (including parenting, if relevant to you)?

- How do your cultural, religious, or spiritual values help cultivate resilience in regards to the larger society and issues of our times?

## Down to Earth: *Do It Yourself*

### *Daily Rituals*

All cultures have some embedded connection to nature. Sometimes people look outside of themselves for a connection that feels spiritual. What do you know about your cultural history and ancestry? Are there elements of your tradition that are connected to the natural world? What is something that your ancestors did—ritual, art, food, song—to connect culture and nature? What feels most compelling to you in regards to these traditions or stories?

As we go through our daily lives, there are relatively simple ways we can recall our traditions as we also make our current existence more sacred. There are many ways to do so, including readings and meditations, lighting a candle with intention, the ways in which we prepare food, family songs, prayers, ceremony, or taking a moment to create pause before a meal.

Here are a few more ideas for integrating ritual into your daily life:

Is there a poem, prayer, quote, or other wisdom teaching from your own cultural tradition that inspires you? If you do not have information about your heritage and ancestry, is there one that speaks to you nevertheless? Create a book to gather these. Or, perhaps, add them to an altar in your home. To create new ways of connecting while fostering sense of place, locate a natural object such as tree, rock, body of water, or spot of land near your own home or in a nearby green space that speaks to you. Spend some time there to get to know this space, perhaps while contemplating a quote or prayer from your tradition to connect old and new. If the spot is conducive to doing so, add natural materials, flowers, or art/words on paper. You might do this all at once or over time. Your offerings may be intended to last or disappear.

If you are not already doing so, learn to prepare and eat some of the foods of your tradition. Find a cookbook or recipes that resonate. This may be something you choose to do with friends to share and exchange meals of your traditions. Is there something that you could grow or might find at a local farmers' market to incorporate into a meal reflective of your cultural identity?

## Awaken the Power: *Contemplative Practice*

### *Writing Meditation*

Pick one of the themes below, or come up with your own in a similar vein. Have some nice paper and writing implements nearby. Reflect on the theme you have chosen. Then, simply allow your thoughts to flow on paper for fifteen minutes. Give yourself this whole time, even if there is pause, as it enables more thoughts to arise. This might remain private and something to put on your altar, or you may choose to share it with someone else.

> *Ancestors and traditions*
>
> *Places where you feel most whole and alive*
>
> *Harmony and/or disconnect between your spiritual practice and your cultural origins*

### *Ten Ways To Initiate or Sustain a Contemplative Practice*

- Choose one practice (meditation, movement, yoga, chanting, silent prayer) to explore, and learn some of its history.

- Create a sacred space or a simple altar for your practice.

- Find simple ways to visit a practice through the day to refresh (such as a two-minute breathing meditation).

- Gain inspiration from traditional or current teachings (books are good), but don't get swept away by spiritual consumerism.

- Practice with consistency—whatever that is for you—alone or with others.

- Find others who share a common or different practice and share experiences.

- Take time for retreats, alone and/or with your partner.

- Connect your practice to nature; bring nature to your practice.

- Change up your practice if it becomes redundant.

- At times, dedicate your spiritual practice to a person or event. in need of healing

*Chapter Eight*

# From Our Farm Table: Seasonal Recipes (and stories) to Feed and Love People

## Before Basil There's Still Pesto

One of the many great things about growing garlic is that it is a three-season edible crop. Garlic is planted in the fall. Bulbs are divided into cloves with the papery covers left intact then planted about six inches apart, three inches deep, covered with a nice layer of compost and then mulch hay. The larger cloves are prioritized for the best bulbs, so we toss the really small cloves into the paths between the garden beds. When the snow melts as spring arrives, the shoots of the main crop emerge (so do the small ones in the paths, as well as the clumps of garlic greens from any bulbs accidentally left from the previous year harvest).

These garlic greens provide one-stop pesto shopping. We blend the greens with olive oil, Parmesan cheese and walnuts, pine nuts or pumpkin seeds (which make a creamy substitute for dairy). Come June, there is another culinary treat: the scapes are the central stalk of hardnecked garlic varieties that form a curl. It is good to cut these when they emerge in order to send the energy down to produce a larger bulb, rather than into the flower bud that the scape will become if left alone (which are nice in a bouquet if you grow lots of garlic and neglect cutting some!). The scapes can then be chopped for a stir-fry or into scrambled eggs, or blended just like the greens to make pesto. We once gave some to a chef who used them as a skewer for grilled scallops. A local Korean woman calls four times a day during scape season to ask if they are ready yet. She and a few family members arrive with huge plastic bags to harvest and then pickle them for their church. We give them free range of the scapes and for no charge as their harvest helps with this needed and time-consuming task. They've learned we love kimchi and bring us some freshly made, and also enjoy scolding us good naturedly, complaining if the scapes (which emerge at slightly different times due to different garlic varieties and planting dates) are not the perfect tenderness.

Looking to make pesto of things that are ready at the same time, I combined arugula, spinach, garlic greens and some fresh mint. Yum! It is a great use of arugula that is a bit gone by: not quite tender enough for salad, and on the spicier side. The spinach mellows the flavor and makes the blend a beautiful green. That recipe is the one we'll share now, but garlic lovers might choose to keep it pure. Any pesto is delicious on pasta, on a baguette, or with grilled chicken or fish.

### Ingredients:

1 cup each of arugula and spinach

4 or 5 garlic leaves, scapes, or a couple of cloves (if using garlic leaves from plants you are cultivating for the bulb, only take one from each plant so as not to deter growth)

1/2 cup olive oil

1/2 cup Parmesan or Romano cheese

1/3 cup of your choice: walnuts, pumpkin or sunflower seeds, almonds, cashews, or pine nuts

Some fresh mint or lemon balm leaves (optional)

*De-stem arugula and spinach and put into a food processor with all of the other ingredients. Blend until smooth, adding salt and pepper to taste, and adjusting other ingredients as necessary to make your favorite blend and consistency. Try other wild and cultivated greens; there is no end to pesto pleasure. Spring greens should tide you over until basil pesto season!*

## Nettle Neighborhood Soup

They will sting you if you aren't paying attention, and nourish you if you are. Spring nettles, what a gift! Fresh and steamed, they lose their prickly charge and result in a great green to add to casseroles and soups, or enjoy with a drizzle of olive oil, salt, and pepper. Dried for tea, the common stinging nettle (*Urtica dioica*) can alleviate allergies and is good for kidneys. I enjoy nettle and oatstraw with a little honey for a bedtime tea, or sip on it cool through the day, especially when I am feeling a bit depleted. An unused window screen propped up on either side for air flow makes a great herb drying rack.

After I gave birth, my dear friend and herbalist Kuumba brought me a creamy soup of nettles, potatoes, and other wild greens that gave my kidneys just what they needed (this was my second meal—the first, after sixty hours of labor, was perfectly fried chicken and a delicious red potato salad from our son's godmother, a meal that I will never forget). If you don't have fresh nettles growing wild, ask around, as others might know of patches to share. And, you can certainly substitute another green like spinach, or an edible weed like lamb's quarters from your spring garden in the soup recipe below. You cut nettles into your harvest basket with scissors and gloves, but some say if you say please-and-thanks, they don't sting as much—always good to give thanks for plant food and medicine anyway!

We call this a neighborhood nettle soup since it incorporates milk from our friends Rachel and Bruce's amazing raw milk dairy Little White Goat, a couple of miles down the road. A spring soup of wild nettles, blended with the last of the stored potatoes and goat milk, served with cornbread, a spring salad, and some hard-boiled eggs is a celebration of the beautiful place and neighborhood we are blessed to call home.

## Ingredients:

A dozen or so stalks of nettles, harvested when tender

4 or 5 potatoes

A small onion or wintered-over leek

A few garlic greens (or a clove or two)

2 cups of goat milk (or cow's milk or non-dairy, if preferred)

Additional water, vegetable, or chicken broth to thin (optional)

Butter, ghee (clarified butter), or olive oil

Salt and pepper to taste

*Rinse nettles and put them in enough water just to cover them. Simmer until tender, then let them cool, chopping them a bit. You can save and drink the water or add it to thin your soup if you don't mind the green tint. Roughly slice or dice the nettles, then boil or steam the potatoes. Meanwhile, chop the onion and garlic and sauté in your choice of butter, ghee, or olive oil. Combine these ingredients in a food processor or blender along with the milk. Add more milk, or water/broth to achieve your desired consistency. Add salt and pepper to taste, and perhaps a dollop of miso. Reheat to serve. I like blended soups, but you can also just combine everything in a pot and leave it chunky. Serve with salad and cornbread. Be nourished!*

## That Salad Dressing

We love reading the notes from customers on the soil-stained notebook in our farm stand, kept there for IOUs and messages. The first tender lettuce, arugula, and spinach greens of the year are ready in the hoop houses at the end of March. When Ricky puts them in the solar- powered farm stand refrigerator and the 'open' signs go up, folks flock here like those who have been deprived of anything green for months. Ah, spring! How delightful it is when snow tires finally come off, the long underwear gets stored in the bottom drawer, and there are bowls of greens on the table for every meal. The customers (many friends and neighbors) that visit our self-serve farm stand leave sweet messages that read: "So happy to be eating your salad again... I feel alive... THE BEST greens: I ate them all the way home and came right back for more."

Our cut and come again style of growing means that one sowing of salad greens like lettuce, spinach, and arugula might result in ten or more cuttings from a patch. With cut and come again growing, seeds are planted once, often sprinkled over an entire area to grow like a carpet rather than in rows. When they are a few inches tall they are trimmed near to the base. Rather than being pulling out, they are watered again, grow back, and are harvested many times. Cut and come again salad greens are often available in mixes with diverse flavors, colors, and textures. We tell tour visitors and those we teach during workshops that this is a great crop for home, community, and school gardens because greens can be grown three seasons outdoors as well as in containers. And, while a tomato plant takes up a lot of real estate and takes a while to produce (albeit delicious when it does), that same space can provide a lot of servings of salad. In fact, our youth program did a little research to reply to the often-asked question—how much can be grown in a small space? We found that a four-by-eight-foot bed when planted broadcast-style (to make a carpet of greens, rather than rows) with a variety of patches of greens, well-tended (staying on top of successive plantings), can yield 500 modest servings of salad over a three-month season. Wow!

Another "wow!" often comes with our tangy, sweet, simple salad dressing. At home, we make it quickly and drizzle it on right before eating. For events like the North Quabbin Garlic and Arts Festival, we make it in bulk, adding a little finely-chopped garlic to the mix and tossing it lightly into a large bowl of greens to serve as part of our 'garlic lover's plate' of crusty breads and savory dips that we've sold to raise funds for our youth program. A really good olive oil and vinegar make it extra special, but any will do. The secret is in the maple syrup sweetness balancing the tangy balsamic, while not overpowering the flavors of a salad of multicolored and textured greens.

## *Maple Balsamic Salad Dressing*

1 cup olive oil

1/4 cup balsamic vinegar

1–2 Tbsp maple syrup (to taste; honey can be used instead)

1 tsp Dijon mustard

A pinch each of salt and pepper

*Shake or blend all ingredients well by hand or emulsify in a blender.*

Options for a twist (choose one, not all at the same time!):

Substitute fresh lemon juice or rice wine vinegar for balsamic or

Add a tablespoon of tahini (sesame paste) or

Add a little beet puree or

Add 1 tsp of crushed garlic or

Add some fresh herbs like mint or oregano

## SOLful Pasta

No matter how many times we tell the kids in our Seeds of Leadership Garden program for local youth to eat breakfast before they arrive for our weekly session, most will not. This is either because they are late to catch the van, they are teenagers and don't eat nourishing things at consistent times, or because their family does not have any food at home. So by the time we've worked a couple of hours in the garden, they are hungry! Each year we write grants and seek donations to fund the program so that it's free for kids and their families, but we still need to stretch a budget to feed lunch to twenty-five youth and staff. And, it has to be on the picnic table quickly once we break. Plus, we want to incorporate as much of the food they are growing themselves as possible because, as one teen said, "I ate my first vegetable ever here." Each week a few youth volunteer to help prepare the lunch. There is always a salad, and then we'll put out fresh carrots and steam or sauté some chard or kale. And at least once a season a chocolate beet cake! But the pasta dish is the economic anchor, the crowd pleaser, and a filling dish. A few of the favorite combinations are a pasta (often pesto pasta!) tossed with fresh tomatoes, basil, and Parmesan cheese and a pasta with peanut sauce, snap peas, and grated carrots.

Depending on the day, we make the pasta early that morning before the kids arrive, or cook it while a small crew is prepping the ingredients that will be tossed with it later. Assuming most people will not be cooking for twenty-five, ingredients in the recipe below serve four to five people. Multiply up for large crowds! Here are two ways we make and enjoy pasta at SOL Garden.

*Pre-cook 1 pound of your choice of pasta (we recommend bow ties, penne, or fusilli). This basic basil pesto recipe will work for a pound of pasta. Blend until smooth:*

2 cups fresh basil leaves

1/2 cup Parmesan or Romano cheese

1/3 cup walnuts

1/2 cup olive oil

2–3 cloves of garlic

Add salt and pepper to taste.

*Toss pasta to coat and add chopped fresh tomatoes. If you don't want to make pesto, pasta tossed in chopped tomatoes, basil leaves, olive oil and cheese is perfectly delicious. Alternately, peanut sauce is a great way for kids to think differently about a common food staple, peanut butter.*

## Sesame Peanut Sauce

In a blender or food processor, combine:

1 cup of peanut butter

1 cup of water or tea (made with a chai tea bag)

2 Tbsp tamari

2 Tbsp rice vinegar

2 tsp sesame oil

2 tsp powdered or fresh ginger

1 Tbsp sugar or honey

Optional: pinch or two of cayenne.

*Adjust seasonings as desired, thin with more water as need. Serve over pasta and top with grated carrots and fresh or lightly-steamed snap peas, broccoli, or string beans. Sprinkle with sesame seeds.*

## We Ate Kale Before it was Cool

Teens will eat food they grow and prepare together.

We never imagined that there would be such a demand for kale that getting seed for the now-popular curled varieties would be a farmer's challenge—let alone that it would appear on the menu of fast food restaurant chains. When we set up at local farmers' markets with our youth program years ago, we had to repeatedly explain to people what kale was and how to use it.

Kale is indeed a great and nutritious crop for the Northeast climate. It keeps on giving three seasons a year, and is especially yummy after an autumn frost makes it tender and sweet. A group of family childcare providers that we worked with to create gardens at their sites once came over for a workshop and saw the Lacinato (also called "dinosaur kale") growing and were intrigued. We generally plant the more typical curly-leaf variety with them and they use it to make kale chips with the young children. I explained that it was a little stronger in flavor so I wasn't sure they would like it, but they'd already started nibbling a leaf, and each left with a bunch to try in the kids' lunches the next day.

One of our summer activities with the local teens in our SOL Garden is to make and serve a farm-to-table meal for eighty folks facing hunger who are regulars at the church downtown, coming for the free meal served there twice a week. On our appointed day we serve pasta with lots of our garden veggies and local chicken, pesto garlic bread, a raw kale salad, and homemade cake with freshly picked berries. We give our raw kale dish a palatable name: "Lemony Cranberry Kale Salad." While the simplest way to prepare kale is steaming then tossing it with olive oil, finely chopped garlic, a little lemon, and salt and pepper, there are many ways to use this excellent and nourishing leafy green in soup, salads, and casseroles. And don't even get us started on green smoothies! The back of our SOL Garden program t-shirt even reads: *We Ate Kale before it was Cool!* These are not homeschooled, organic baby-food-raised kids, but now they can grow, prepare, share, and eat a big bowl of kale...together.

### *Lemony Cranberry Kale Salad*

A really big bunch of kale (or at least 12–15 big kale leaves)

1/2 cup shaved Parmesan

1/2 cup pumpkin seeds

1/2 cup dried cranberries

4 Tbsp extra virgin olive oil

2 Tbsp honey or maple syrup

2 lemons

Sea salt and pepper to taste

*De-stem kale and tear into small pieces, and place into a large mixing bowl. Squeeze the juice of the lemons over the kale, and then massage it until quite tender. Whisk together the honey and olive oil. Drizzle over the kale, and then add cheese, nuts, and dried fruit. Toss everything together with sea salt and freshly cracked black pepper to taste. Top with some additional shaved Parmesan. Be creative: substitute any nuts for the pumpkin seeds, or other dried fruit like chopped dates or apricots for the cranberries.*

## Cheap, Tasty Soup

People say that 'natural, organic' food is expensive. Well, it is if you buy pre-made ready-to-cook foods, or are looking at the price tag on natural snack foods. These are tasty but can give the wrong impression about the cost of healthy food to those new to making their own. I like the expression "If it wasn't food 100 years ago, it isn't food now" in regards to keeping processed food out of one's diet. And, if it *was* food 100 years ago, it is still food now—and often the healthiest, most economical food one can grow, buy, and prepare.

I make a lot of one-pot, bean-based soups. They are great to have on hand for our family for the week, or to serve farm volunteers or people who happen to arrive. I keep a variety of either bulk-purchased or our own grown dried beans on hand in jars in the pantry. A standard assortment includes: black beans, kidney or pinto, French lentils, red lentils, split peas, and maybe a navy or cannellini white bean. I soak the beans the night before, say on Sunday. Monday morning I rinse them and get them cooking, adding whatever vegetables and grains we have in the garden, fridge, or pantry. It takes just a few minutes to add in few handfuls of chopped onions, some garlic, carrots or celery with some salt and pepper as the beans cook. A handful of sea vegetables like nori, dulse, or kelp are great to add, too—and so nutritious. When the beans are close to ready, add in some diced or sliced potatoes, sweet potatoes, and greens like chard, kale and spinach. Before serving, a dollop of miso adds health, flavor, and richness.

Here are some favorite bean/veggie soup combinations; garlic and onions can go in pretty much everything. Experiment with your favorite fresh or dried herbs, too.

- Red lentils (one of the few that you don't need to soak in advance) with sweet potato, spinach, and coconut milk
- Kidney beans with cubed squash, leeks, and kale or broccoli
- Black beans with carrots, potatoes, chard, and a touch of hot pepper and cumin
- French or regular lentils with carrots, celery, and dried apricot or cranberries
- Split peas with carrots and/or sweet potato. Eat sausage or bacon? Add a little!
- Navy or cannellini beans with zucchini or yellow summer squash and wild or red rice

*Other favorite, non-bean focused soup combos for smaller crowds:*

- Barley with shiitake or wild-harvested mushroom, celery, and miso
- Carrot soup with ginger (and/or fennel), pureed with cream or coconut milk
- Chilled local yogurt with any berries and fresh mint
- Potato and leek: steam or boil potatoes, sauté leeks, blend with vegetable broth and/or goat or cow milk. Purple Peruvian potatoes with leeks is a major "wow!"
- Beef, lamb, or goat stew: cook sautéed, cubed grass-fed meat with onions and garlic, add water to cover, continue to cook on low with potatoes, carrots, and parsnips

- Chicken soup! Use a whole, fresh free-range chicken (or make a broth from a roasted one from last night's dinner; or cook just legs and thighs). Cook chicken with parsley and other herbs (I like adding a little ginger and turmeric for an amazingly healthy and bright soup). Strain the bones out. Bok choy, carrots, leeks, sweet or regular potatoes are all great in chicken soup.

## Eat Your Microbes

While giving a presentation at a local high school, I asked for a show of hands of anyone that had bacteria in their bodies. Hmm, only a few raised theirs, and those who did not frowned. Unfortunately, the anti-bacterial rage has given these essential critters a bad rap, to the point where those students don't equate beneficial bacteria with their health. It is humbling that microbes outnumber human cells in our bodies. There are 500 to 1,000 species of bacteria that live in the large intestine and we call these, collectively, gut flora. One year I couldn't shake a lingering respiratory cough. My very smart friend and naturopathic doctor Amy Rothenberg suggested I get some more probiotics in my body. For a head cold...feed the gut? *Hmm*, I thought. I've definitely noticed increased immunity to colds and such since we have increased our intake of cultured and fermented foods that feed our beneficial microbes and introduce a variety of probiotics into our gut. Plus, raw goat milk kefir, miso, and lacto-fermented veggies are so delicious! Here are a few simple things we love. We won't get into making lacto-fermented foods and beverages (such as kombucha) here, but it is a fairly easy thing for individuals to learn to do in an affordable way. And there are also great small companies out there—a little fermented food and drink goes a long way. Get your health from real food and herbs whenever possible. Even a tablespoon of some fermented food each day is good food and good medicine.

*Make these simple snacks or light meals using fermented and cultured foods:*

*Kefir or Yogurt Lassi:* Blend fresh or frozen seasonal fruit with kefir or yogurt (preferably made with local, raw milk). Use a quantity of each that pleases you. Add a dash of sea salt and maple syrup to taste.

*For a Summer Soup*, do the same but instead of fruit blend in a scallion, cucumber, some fresh mint and/or parsley, and salt and pepper. So very refreshing!

*Simple Miso Soup*: Our favorite miso comes from Swift River Miso, made with great integrity and in blends such as garlic red pepper and dandelion leek. Sauté an onion or leek and a little garlic in a bit of olive oil. A bit of turmeric and ginger (powdered or fresh) would be good here. Add a cup or two of veggies such as diced carrots, daikon, celery, broccoli and shiitake mushrooms. Add a quart of water and let cook. This is a good time to add in some cubes of firm tofu and some kale torn into small pieces, and even

Good food is food medicine!

some dulse or other seaweed. When veggies are tender, stir in two tablespoons of miso, more or less to taste. Do not boil your soup once miso is in.

*If you eat meat*, I would follow basically the same process, but start by simmering a marrow bone from grass-fed beef for many hours. A little vinegar in the cooking water helps get the good stuff out of the bone. Then add the veggies, spices, and miso.

*Sauerkraut or Kimchi Quesadilla*: Warm a corn or flour tortilla in a pan, putting on some grated cheese, avocado, and a few dollops of raw fermented sauerkraut or kimchi (both among the easiest fermented foods to make) when it comes off the pan. Add a side of rice and cooked greens for a very hearty meal. Dollop with cultured sour cream or yogurt before serving. Kimchi is also super great in a veggie or pastrami Reuben. Make your sandwich sauce using yogurt and sriracha (a tasty fermented condiment)!

## Garlic Lover's Plate: A Festival Tradition

The banner that hangs on the front of the table under the Seeds of Solidarity tent at our North Quabbin Garlic and Arts Festival reads: "Garlic Lover's Plate, Farm Fresh Salad. Eat Here, Support Youth Gardens!" We are finally here after a long season; the festival weekend arrives after many weeks of setting up canopies, directional and parking signs, compost/recycle stations, and more. And, after many months of building trust and gardening and cooking skills among a group of our SOL Garden teenagers, we are here and ready to sell some

good garlic food! We tried some crazy things over the years, running food booths near and far to provide the youth with this experience, plus make some funds to run this program. There was the year we rented a big grill and kept it stoked with wood briquettes to serve salmon burgers with garlic sauce, garlic grilled cheese, and garlic PB&J sandwiches while the rain poured in the gaps between two ragtag canopies. For a couple of summers we signed on to run a food booth at Solarfest, loading up the van with a crew of totally inexperienced kids and the makings for burritos and fried potato pancakes prepared on stoves running on biodiesel—tested for the first time when we set up our stand.

The Garlic Lover's Plate was a fall festival standard for many years, delicious and manageable. The plate consists of three pieces of focaccia or similar bread, each with a different topping. The first is garlic bread (a mix of chopped scapes reserved and frozen from spring, freshly harvested garlic, and fresh chopped parsley, warmed in virgin olive oil. The second features a smoked salmon spread which is super easy but impressive. And the nice thing about the third, a tapenade, is that you can incorporate crops and flavors doing well in the garden, so long as the namesake ingredient—capers or 'tapenas'—as well as olives are present. Nicely plated, with a salad of mixed greens freshly harvested from the farm and topped with the last of the Carmen peppers and Sungold cherry tomatoes, a nasturtium flower and our signature vinaigrette (see "That Salad Dressing") with some finely chopped garlic. Once I make the stuff and set it up, one staff and several of our youth take over, rotating two shifts during each day. Two don gloves to make and serve, one practices math at the cashbox. All share enthusiasm and encourage Seeds of Solidarity 'Awaken the Power to Grow Food Everywhere' t-shirt sales to go along with that plate and raise funds for yet another year of SOL Garden.

*These recipes yield about a quart of each spread.*

### Smoked Salmon Garlic Spread

*Roast a bulb of garlic and squeeze out pulp, or simply use 3 medium, raw cloves. In a food processor blend:*

One 8 oz package of cream cheese

4 oz of Greek yogurt

4–6 oz of smoked salmon with the garlic

1–2 Tbsp of lemon juice and a hearty sprinkle of black pepper

*Adjust seasonings—salt should not be needed with the salmon, but add if desired.*

### Harvest Tapenade

Blend one pound of pitted kalamata olives (rinsed)

1 heaping tablespoon of capers (rinsed)

3 cloves of garlic

1–2 Tbsp of good olive oil

A small bunch of arugula

1 diced fresh red pepper,

About 1/2 cup of fresh basil leaves

A little salt and pepper to taste

Enough olive oil for easy spreading

Optional: 1/2 cup of roasted eggplant

## Winter Roasted Roots

The trees are bare of leaves. The festival is over and the garlic is replanted for the season. The kids are back at school. The youth program is on hiatus from weekly activity with just a few leadership events here and there. Our farm visiting day season is over and the frequency of calls, requests, and orders diminish. The root cellar is stocked with winter squash, carrots, garlic, onions, beets, potatoes, and a few giant Gilfeather turnips. A fire in the wood stove takes the chill off at the end of the day, and is enough to keep us cozy through the night. It's time for Roasted Roots. Often. They are great for dinner alone or with a salad or protein, and the leftovers are delicious mixed with eggs for breakfast, or pureed into a creamy soup for the next day's lunch or dinner.

*Gather your roots, squash and tubers. A nice combination is:*

1 medium butternut or 2 delicata squash

5 or 6 potatoes

4 carrots

1 sweet potato and/or a couple of parsnips

1 medium turnip or rutabaga

1 large onion

1 bulb (or more) of garlic

Olive oil to toss

Freshly ground salt and pepper

*We love roasted beets, but roast them separately and add at the end if you wish to include.*

*Prepare and cut all veggies however you like them. A mix of cubed, sliced, and diced is fine. Peel the squash if using butternut. Keeping the skin on everything else is fine so long as you grew it or if someone else did without chemicals.*

*Separate the garlic cloves but do not remove the papery covers. Toss everything (including the garlic cloves) lightly with olive oil to coat, sprinkle on some coarse salt and freshly ground pepper and some dried herbs like oregano, parsley or basil, too, if you wish. Bake in a roasting pan at about 375 degrees for a good hour or so, until everything is tender. If you do this in a single layer, stuff will have a bit of a crisp—if a few inches deep, less so. Some things cook faster than others, which is okay. If you don't like this, cook everything separately then mix them together at the end.*

This is a great dish as is, with a side of steamed greens, with roast or grilled chicken, or with baked or broiled fish. Cornbread also makes a great companion to roasted roots.

If you have leftovers here is how you can enjoy them the next day. For either of these, you'll want to squeeze the roasted garlic out of their wrappers first.

Heat up leftovers a bit then whisk up some eggs for a hearty breakfast, or roll into corn tortillas.

To make soup: heat the roasted veggies up with some water to cover, and then blend with an immersion blender, adding some milk for a creamy soup. Season to taste if needed. We eat roasted roots a lot in fall and winter and are always asked to bring them to family holiday meals, too.

## Honoring Corn

Corn, or maize, is held as sacred in many traditions. It was cultivated by indigenous people in what is now Mexico as much as 10,000 years ago from a wild grass called teosinte. Corn is a staple for many worldwide, and a key crop for resilience. But corn gets a bad rap as one of the crops most heavily targeted by Monsanto and other GMO-pushing, seed-thieving corporations. Plus, much of the genetically modified corn grown is used for animal feed and high fructose corn syrup. High fructose corn syrup is high on the list of ingredients in nutritionally vacuous processed foods and drinks; its agribusiness growth parallels the rise in obesity and type 2 diabetes. Corn has been altered and maligned. But growing traditional, deeply nourishing corn keeps true seeds alive and shared.

We've been growing traditional Narragansett corn seed from Whit Davis, as well as Blue Hopi Corn, Osage Red, and Glass Gem. When monks and nuns of the Japanese Buddhist order Nipponzan Myohoji came to the U.S. in 1978 at the invitation of members of the American Indian Movement to join the Longest Walk, our friends Brother Kato Shonin and Sister Clare requested a circle planting of Narragansett corn at the Leverett Peace Pagoda. It thrived with compost, cardboard, and fish emulsion. That they and many amazing people pray in the nearby temple and have held ceremonies on that land probably doesn't hurt either.

We use the corn we grow to make cornbread for supper, and corn cereal in the morning. It can be made into tortillas with a little extra work, and also for polenta recipes or whole in posole stew. If you do not grow your own, buy some organic stone-ground cornmeal from a farmer or co-op. We enjoy it often, especially with our wonderful staff and farm interns during our end-of-season gratitude gathering.

### *Really Good Cornbread*

1/4 cup of honey

1 cup of buttermilk (or equivalent of milk and yogurt)

1 egg

1 cup cornmeal

1 cup unbleached flour

2 tsp baking powder

1/2 tsp baking soda

1/2 tsp salt

3 Tbsp melted butter

Optional when in season: 1/2 cup of fresh sweet corn

*Preheat oven to 425 degrees. Beat together egg, buttermilk, and honey. In a separate bowl, mix together all the dry ingredients. Combine the wet and dry ingredients and the melted butter. Mix by hand until just blended. Stir in the fresh corn if you are using. Pour into a greased 8-inch square pan or cast iron skillet and bake until golden, 20–30 minutes.*

## *Field Guide for Chapter Eight:*
## *From Our Farm Table: Seasonal Recipes*
## *(and stories) to Feed and Love People*

## Questions to Ponder: Health and Nourishment

- If you grow food, how do or could you share these skills or abundance with friends, neighbors, or other people in need of physical and spiritual nourishment?

- What is one recipe or meal that you count on because it keeps tradition alive, or is healthy, simple, or economical? How can you share this knowledge with others?

- Are your values aligned with the places where you access or purchase food? Are there ways in which you can push your edge? (For some, this might mean taking the time to purchase more bulk food at a co-op, or prioritize weekly shopping at a local farmers' market—for others, drying, canning, gleaning, making your own herbal teas, or dumpster diving might be on your list).

- What do you have more than enough of in your kitchen that you might pass on to others?

- What do you need in order to prepare more of what you consume, slowly and economically?

- Do you have food-growing or preparation skills to contribute to your community to support nutrition and wellness among those in need? Think of a social service agency, religious institution, or school that you might reach out to as a volunteer.

## Down to Earth: *Do it Yourself*

### *Basics for the Farm-Fresh Kitchen*

The items on this list may be passed on from others, received as gifts, handmade (bowls and platters), or found at tag sales or thrift stores. We work to shape a kitchen that is minimalist, efficient, and beautiful. These are a few things we reach for often, especially when serving farm-fresh vegetables or feeding family, friends, or large groups.

**Bowls:** A set of nested mixing bowls, stainless steel, ceramic, or glass.

Four or five beautiful serving bowls—a combination of handmade pottery and wooden is lovely. There may be four bowls on your dinner table passed at any given time, so a range in sizes from small for a dip to large for a salad is great.

**Platters:** A rough-edge piece of wood or slate is great for cheeses or other appetizers, something shallow for meat or pasta or slices of bread.

**Knives:** One utility knife (five-inch blade or so), one large chef's knife, one paring knife, and one bread knife. Invest in a few good knives, be they steel or ceramic, and find the one that feels good in your hand. Or, find old ones at thrift stores that can be sharpened. A mandoline slicer is a great tool, too. Have a few cutting boards of your favorite material (wood and bamboo are nice).

**Pots:** One cast-iron pan, enameled cast-iron covered pot (7 qt. is a great size), one or two saucepans with lids, a large pot for pasta or big soups and such, and a steamer that fits within.

**Pans:** One cookie sheet, one 9-by-12-inch glass or ceramic baking pan and another if you like to roast things, one pie/quiche pan.

**A stainless colander** for rinsing veggies, a finer strainer for rinsing grains, and a salad spinner.

**A tea kettle** and teapot (ceramic or glass).

**Measuring:** One glass, two-cup measuring cup and some smaller ones, and a set of stainless steel measuring cups and spoons. Bread bakers will want a scale.

**An assortment** of mixing spoons, spatula, whisk, kitchen scissors, and tongs kept on your counter near the stove.

**Appliances:** A Vitamix and/or a food processor, or an immersion or regular blender.

## Awaken the Power: *Contemplative Practice*

### *Meal Blessing*

There are so many ways to bless a meal before eating. The most common around our table is to simply pause and hold hands (or touch elbows if it's cold and flu season!) before eating. It is also quite lovely to bring your palms together at the heart, take a few breaths in this position, then open your hands palms down above your plate for a few more breaths before eating your delicious and nourishing meal (now made even more so!).

We also keep a few books near our table—we like Thich Nhat Hanh and there are two small gems of books, *How to Eat* and *How to Love,* that we read from. We also have books with an earth-connected short writing or blessing from a diversity of cultures for each day. It often seems like the one we open to is just right for that day! Draw from any number of books, songs, or poems that appeal to you. You may even wish to create an activity with friends or family where you each choose a meaningful quote, passage, or poem relevant to food, farming, and wellness. Have a party where you share and decorate these individual pages, then compile and reproduce them so that everyone has a copy of the collection to use at their own tables (this makes a great gift).

The main idea is to pause before eating to appreciate the food before you, the lands and labor and energy that has gone into bringing it to you, as well as to contemplate those without food. Here is one of our favorite pieces, a Nicaraguan blessing, to read and contemplate:

> *Dale pan a aquellos que tienen hambre,*
> *y danos hambre de justicia a nosotros que tenemos pan.*
> *May there be bread for those who hunger,*
> *and hunger for justice for those of us who have bread.*

## *Ten Ways To Practice Food Love*

- Eat in season, and primarily plants.
- Make your table beautiful.
- Prepare and linger over meals with friends.
- Make and/or consume fermented foods.
- Use plenty of fresh, dried, or wildcrafted herbs.
- Consider food as medicine (and try actively making some tinctures or infused oils).
- Relearn how to prepare and eat traditional foods, from your own culture and those of others.
- Purchase bulk items (shop at co-ops) for less packaging and waste.
- Cook simple food in quantity for the week and lower-cost lunches.
- Donate from your garden, and/or prepare and serve nourishing food for soup kitchens.

# Epilogue

## *Onward with Love*

Some things have changed. Some remain the same.

We completed the book you hold in your hands—twenty-four years after our marriage day and thirty-four years after our first night of young love under the grape arbor at the New Alchemy Institute where we met. Given the intention of the book, it felt right and ceremonial to meet with our publisher to go over all of the book's components on our actual wedding anniversary. And yes, we then enjoyed a romantic dinner together afterwards.

As this book goes to press, we also mark some other significant anniversaries: the twentieth year of both the North Quabbin Garlic and Arts Festival and our program for local youth, SOL Garden, which was the springboard for our many other youth and community food justice programs. We mark time, and consider the shape of our next phase of relationship, service, and action.

Committing memories and stories to paper has been personally evocative. Looking back at the whole of techniques, programs, and relationships we cultivated over the years helps us look forward to how we can sow seeds of solidarity in new ways. We are excited to hit the road a bit to offer book readings and interactive workshops for community organizations and colleges with burgeoning food and farm programs to share methods, programs, and curricula that promote climate and food justice.

Our daily walks not only exercise our farm dog and keep us attuned to nature, but also generate ideas. One is another book—a wellness survival guide and cookbook—that emanates from our current work with men and women who are incarcerated, and people in recovery. Thinking more globally, over the years we have had visitors from around the world who carry our farming and educational methods back to their homes. Copies from the draft of this book are in our bags as we go to Cuba and share regenerative, no-till methods. Our intern and friend Sta plans to return to Zimbabwe to promote food and economic resilience, and we are excited to partner to support her efforts.

It is our desire and intention to continue to make and magnify love through our ways of being, ways of farming, and, especially, by sharing widely what we have practiced, innovated, and learned. We are blessed to have found each other, and passion and purpose. This book, and whatever may come from it, is our prayer and our offering, and the best way we know to pass it forward.

# Acknowledgments

This book is both a labor of love and expression of love. The list of all of those to thank is too vast for these pages, as it includes many who offered inspiration and mentorship, and the thousands whose journeys brought them to our programs and farm to learn and share, or us to their homes and lands.

Our parents, siblings, extended family and good friends have wondered for many years what we could possibly be up to next, and offered great love and faith in us over the years. A shout-out to the Seeds of Solidarity board and staff, interns all along the way, and supporters near and far. When we first walked the long-abandoned land that would blossom into Seeds of Solidarity, in a community we did not know, we could not have imagined that our neighbors would not only be supportive of our wild ideas, but become valued friends and collaborators. The most humongous initiative, and a highlight of our community work, has been co-creating the North Quabbin Garlic and Arts Festival with an amazing group of people, together shaping a creative, joyful, and resilient microcosm of the world we believe is possible. We could not have done anything that is expressed in these pages in isolation, or without beloved community near and far.

We are farmers and educators much more than writers. We didn't know exactly where and how to start this book. Our friend and accomplished writer Mira Bartók sat with us at the beginning and shared two pearls of wisdom that served as guides. She suggested we write a bunch of first lines for stories, then let them grow. When we wondered if and why anyone would care about our experiences, she reminded us that personal stories well-told can be universal. Once we had a rough draft, we shared ideas and excerpts with some wonderful writers and thinkers to get initial feedback. Many thanks to Sara Elinoff Acker, MaryKate Despres, Liz Gemme, Dan Habib, Mim Habib, Terry Jenoure, Betsy McNamara, AnnMarie Meltzer, Diane Nassif, Sonia Nieto, Kim Tait, Karen Traub, and Jonathan Von Ranson for their insights which were an immense help and shower of support. Lou Leelyn gifted her skills with social media, spreading the good word along with many nuggets of inspiration. As we neared the finish line, those who read our words and offered advance praise collectively created a tapestry of words that fill our hearts and offer diverse perspectives on what they found meaning-ful, and put their well-earned credentials and love-stamp on the book for future readers.

We are fortunate to have an amazing publisher, one so aligned with values we embrace. Many thanks to worker-owned Levellers Press for great attentiveness and skill, and making what could be a nerve-wracking process personal and pleasurable. Special thanks to Anna Mullen for fabulous editing, and Steve Strimer for his orchestration and craftsmanship. Lynne Rudié has long done the graphic design for Seeds of Solidarity outreach materials and her cover design is a great gift. The cover mandala art is by our son Levi who makes our story complete. He and his generation give us much reason for hope.

We are farmers reliant on the land for livelihood, and have long felt held and healed by nature. We are grateful for that which is seen and unseen, and supports and sustains all life. We recognize and feel deeply the struggles and courage of our own ancestors and all those worldwide seeking only to live simply and in peace. We recognize and feel deeply the fact that we dwell and farm on land that was not origi-nally of our family, but of the Nipmuc people.

Our curiosity, creativity, and faith are recharged daily by the won-ders of the natural world and divine forces that surround and abound. We give thanks for the magic and synchronicity that brought us togeth-er and keeps us together in shared vision and which magnifies the most powerful force of all, love.

## *Timeline: Our Lives/Big Picture Influences*

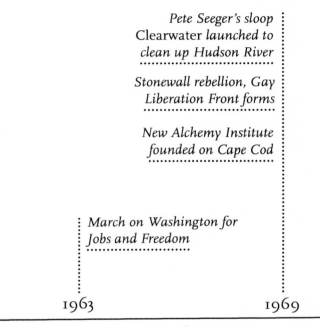

*Pete Seeger's sloop*
Clearwater *launched to*
*clean up Hudson River*

*Stonewall rebellion, Gay*
*Liberation Front forms*

*New Alchemy Institute*
*founded on Cape Cod*

*March on Washington for*
*Jobs and Freedom*

1963            1969

1962        1964        1972

*Civil Rights Act of 1964*

Deb and Ricky are born
100 miles apart

*Rachel Carson's* Silent
Spring *published*

*Cesar Chavez and Dolores*
*Huerta found union which*
*will become United Farm*
*Workers*

Ricky visits sloop
*Clearwater* with his sixth
grade class

Deb visits the New
Alchemy Institute on a
family vacation

Ricky crews on
the *Clearwater*
......................

Deb studying
Environmental Design
at University of
Colorado Boulder
......................

*OPEC's oil embargo
begins energy crisis*
......................

*E. F. Schumacher's* Small
is Beautiful: A Study of
Economics As If People
Mattered *published*
......................

1973                    1981

1978                          1982          1984

*American Indian
Movement begins The
Longest Walk to support
tribal sovereignty*
......................

*Northeast Organic
Farming Association
founded*
............

Deb and Ricky meet at
New Alchemy Institute and
create the first 'Solidarity'
garden together
......................

Deb moves to Western Massachusetts to teach & study environmental and multicultural education

Ricky establishes Jasper's Farm in Interlaken, New York with a NAI buddy

*Alar scare engenders widespread awareness of pesticide dangers*

*Exxon Valdez oil spill off coast of Alaska*

Ricky farms and learns building trade in New York while Deb gets Masters in Environmental Education, pursues yoga and dance studies

*New England Peace Pagoda built in Leverett, Massachusetts*

1985          1987                    1989

          1988                              1990

*First World AIDS Day*

*Gulf War on Iraq begins*

*Nigerian environmental activist Ken Saro-Wiwa executed*

*Inaugural United Nations Climate Change Conference in Berlin*

Dowse and dig well.

Build and move into first structure, the little house, with small solar electric system

Create first garden beds on barren land

Deb and Ricky participate in eight-month Pilgrimage for Peace and Life, Auschwitz to Hiroshima

1995

1997

1994

1996

1998

Deb and Ricky reunite and marry at New England Peace Pagoda

*Anti-Apartheid Movement leads to election of Nelson Mandela*

Build foundation for main house and construct first adjacent greenhouse as Seeds of Solidarity Farm greens business expands with each year

Purchase of land on Chestnut Hill Road, Orange begins Seeds of Solidarity (SOS)

Deb gets Doctorate in Multicultural Education

Group tours and
Solidarity Saturdays begin

Family moves into main house after
three years of building. Install main
solar electric system for home & farm

First year of farm
apprentices at SOS

We get our first biodiesel
vehicle, a 1980 Mercedes

*September 11 attacks*

SOS Education Center
programs begin with
year one of Seeds of
Leadership Garden.

First big (USDA)
federal grant received
launches SOS school
gardens, farm-to-school,
newsletters, and more

First Annual North Quabbin
Garlic and Arts Festival

Our son Levi is born!

1999                              2001              2003

2000                                      2004

SOS Education
Center receives
501(c)(3)status

Garlic and Arts Festival
expands and moves to
nearby Forster Farm

*U.S. Department of
Agriculture takeover of
organic certification*

*National Farm to School
Network authorized
(network began in 90s)*

Field acreage increases,
several more greenhouses
built and in production,
sales expand to many
restaurants, markets

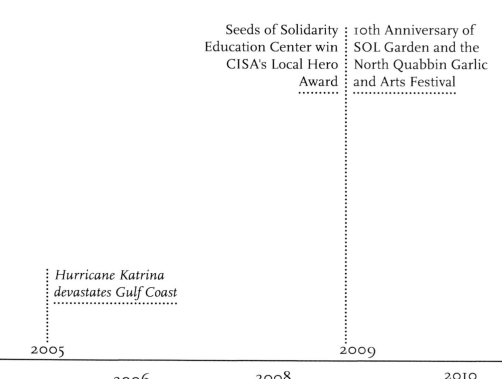

Seeds of Solidarity : 10th Anniversary of
Education Center win : SOL Garden and the
CISA's Local Hero : North Quabbin Garlic
Award : and Arts Festival

*Hurricane Katrina*
*devastates Gulf Coast*

2005

2009

2006

2008

2010

Initiate Earth and Spirit
Retreats for Adults

Garlic and Arts
Festival expanded
to full weekend.
Dar Williams
benefit concert
helps increase
festival crowds.

Teaching *Grow Food*
*Everywhere* at Omega's
Rhinebeck campus

*U.S. Immigrant*
*Rights Movement*
*mobilizes*

Receive SARE grant to
research cardboard method

Farm shifts to weekly
volunteers rather than
long-term apprentice
program

*Barack Obama*
*elected President*

Youth and community
programs, presentations, and
teaching multiply with more
grants and contributions

First Annual
Community
Food Forum

Widespread farm
deliveries transition to
focus on farm stand, elder
CSA, and local-only sales

SOS no-till and
regenerative methods
included in Cornell Small
Farms Program research

*Black Lives Matter
movement begins*

*Conference of the Parties
to the U.N. Framework
Convention on Climate
Change adopts Paris
Agreement*

2011

2013

2015

2012

2014

Grow Food Everywhere
for Health and Justice
programs (for families,
community gardens,
childcare) begin

Fifty raised bed and
guerrilla gardens now
created in and for
North Quabbin region!

Teach women gardening
and empowerment
programs with local
agencies

Create healing gardens : Family show *Seeking the*
for people in recovery at : *Sacred on the Farm* at
Quabbin Retreat : Augusta Savage Gallery

: Levi graduates high
: school and goes to college

2017

2016                              2018

                                 20th Anniversary of
*Magnify Your Love*              North Quabbin Garlic
workshop launches               and Arts Festival
at Omega
                                 20th Anniversary of SOL
First Waking up with            Garden program for youth
the Land Ceremony at
Seeds of Solidarity

*Dakota Access Pipeline*
*Protests peak at Standing*
*Rock Indian Reservation*

Begin teaching gardening
class at Franklin County Jail